The IRONSTONE QUARRIES of the MIDLANDS

History, Operation and Railways

Part VII

Rutland

by
Eric Tonks
M.Sc., F.R.I.C., Dip.Maths.

Book Law Publications
Nottingham

© Eric Tonks 1989

ISBN 978-1-907094-06-4

First Published in 1989
by
Runpast Publishing

This Edition Published in 2009
by
Book Law Publications

Printed by The Amadeus Press, Cleckheaton, BD19 4TQ

Ruston Bucyrus shovel loading a train in the charge of one of the Ruston & Hornsby locomotives at Cottesmore quarries. About 1936. (RRM Archives)

CONTENTS

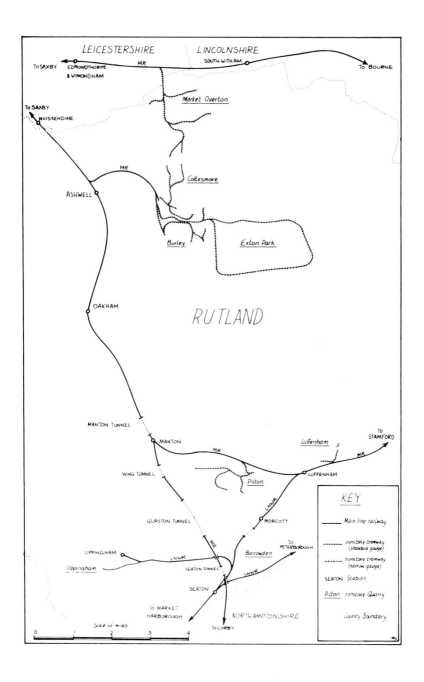

LEICESTERSHIRE   LINCOLNSHIRE

To SAXBY   EDMONDTHORPE   MR   SOUTH WITHAM   To BOURNE
& WYMONDHAM

Market Overton

To SAXBY
WHISSENDINE

MR
Cottesmore

ASHWELL

Burley   Exton Park

OAKHAM

RUTLAND

MANTON TUNNEL

MANTON   MR   Luffenham   TO STAMFORD

WING TUNNEL   Pilton   MR   LUFFENHAM

GLASTON TUNNEL   MORCOTT   LNWR

TO PETERBOROUGH

UPPINGHAM   LNWR   Barrowden

Uppingham   SEATON TUNNEL   LNWR

SEATON

TO MARKET   NORTHAMPTONSHIRE
HARBOROUGH

Scale of miles   TO CORBY

0   1   2   3   4

KEY

—————— Main line railway

++++++++ Ironstone tramway
(standard gauge)

·········· Ironstone tramway
(narrow gauge)

SEATON Station

Pilton Ironstone Quarry

County Boundary

6

INTRODUCTION

In the boundary reorganisation of 1974 Rutland became part of Leicestershire, a logical sequel to the pooling of various administrative functions in preceding years; but people living in Rutland are keen to preserve as much as possible of its independent status, and the Leicestershire authorities, to their credit, have shown an understanding attitude to their smaller neighbour — for example raising no objections to the erection of handsome 'Rutland' road signs at the former county boundaries.

As far as ironstone quarrying was concerned, the two counties differed on almost every count, with few similarities between them in geology, history, ownership or equipment. The Leicestershire quarries — all, save Sproxton and a few minor pits, in the Marlstone — were opened up in the 19th century; they were dominated by the activities of the Holwell Iron Co, the Stanton Ironworks Co Ltd and the Staveley Iron & Coal Co Ltd, all of which laid down a marvellous array of narrow gauge tramways. The quarries were mostly shallow, with hand operation superseded by quarry machines of modest size. In contrast, Rutland's quarries were all in the Northampton Sand ironstone, and all but one started after 1900; there was a wide variety of owners, the tramways were predominantly of standard gauge, and all the quarries had machines, some of them very heavy. Furthermore, quarrying in Rutland had ceased before the county was absorbed into Leicestershire.

In Leicestershire, almost all of the quarries were served by special mineral branches laid by the Midland Railway and Great Northern Railway, and Rutland started off in the same way with the opening of the MR Cottesmore branch in 1882 to serve the quarries there; this branch was utilised by new quarries at Burley (after World War I) and at Exton Park (after World War II). Two more workings were served by the Syston-Peterborough line at Luffenham, and both were opened in 1919, though only one (Pilton) lasted any length of time. The remaining quarries were served by three different main lines—Market Overton by the MR Saxby-Bourne line in 1906, and Uppingham at the end of the LNWR branch in 1912, both by rail; and Barrowden on the LMSR Rugby-Peterborough line in 1942, by lorry haulage. So the quarries in Rutland were fairly widely distributed on to the county rail network. Uppingham was closed as soon as the School authorities could manage it, Luffenham never got going fully, and Barrowden was a very small undertaking; but Cottesmore, Burley, Exton Park, Pilton and Market Overton all lasted until after World War II. Ownership varied; Cottesmore and Exton Park were owned by United Steel Co's Ore Mining Branch, Burley by Bell Bros (later Dorman Long, their only Midland quarry), Market Overton by James Pain, Pilton by Staveley and Barrowden by Naylor Benzon Mining Co Ltd. Market Overton was later owned by Stanton and then by Stewarts & Lloyds Minerals Ltd.

There is plenty in the archives concerning the larger and later quarries, and the only really difficult one is Uppingham, about which almost nothing has survived; we have had to rely on local memory. The group of quarries served by the Cottesmore branch make the most interesting study because of the length of their history—90 years—and the great variety of operating methods they display—the narrow gauge tramway and rope-worked incline operating at Cottesmore until the 1950s, then lorry transport; the little-visited Burley system under its perennial coating of purple calcine dust; and the big circular formation of Exton Park. At the last was the only 'big dragline' of Midlands ironstone other than Corby. Market Overton had quarry machines from 1906 onwards—steam, diesel and electric—and in the chasm of No. 6 quarry it is possible to picture a quarrying scene of the 1970s. Market Overton also featured in a railway preservation scheme that came to grief along with that at nearby Buckminster; but the seed sown there became the far more meaningful preservation effort of the Rutland Railway Museum at Cottesmore, with its strong slant towards the ironstone industry. They extend a welcome to all visitors and I am grateful to them for their help and encouragement.

Acknowledgement is given in the text to people who have supplied particular information, and special thanks are due to Ian Lloyd for his excellent maps; to Martin Davies for his critical checking of the original draft, and for his expert help in copying archive photographs; and to the photographers who have kindly allowed me to use their work. Photographs captioned RRM derive from the archives of the Rutland Railway Museum, to whom special thanks are due.

Birmingham 1989   Eric Tonks

For abbreviations used in the text and for terms used in the tables of locomotives and quarry machines, see 'Explanation of Tables'.

KEY TO INDIVIDUAL QUARRY MAPS

──────────	Main Line Railway
SEATON ══════	Station
+++++++++++++	Ironstone Tramway (Standard gauge)
┴┴┴┴┴┴┴┴┴┴	Ironstone Tramway (Narrow gauge)
┴┴┴┴┴┴┴┴┴┴	Ironstone Tramway (Rope worked incline)
─┘└─	Roads
Pilton	Village
<u>Pilton Quarries</u>	Ironstone Quarry
⌐¯¯¯⌐	Area of Quarry working
☐ Scotts	Quarry Face
↙ 1937 / 1940	Direction of Quarrying and dates of operation

IML

BARROWDEN QUARRIES

Owners: Naylor Benzon Mining Co Ltd.

The entry of Naylor Benzon Mining Co Ltd into the home-producing iron ore industry is described under the Nassington section, but we might here refer to the company's title. When the iron and steel industry was nationalised for the first time the quarries were placed under separate ownership (Nassington Barrowden Mining Co Ltd) as from 3rd January 1951, to enable the Iron & Steel Board to take them over without altering the framework of the parent body. This title was retained under de-nationalisation, though the Barrowden quarries had been closed before the new title came into effect! The choice of the new title itself gives rise to speculation that advantage was taken of the coincidence of the names of the two quarries to formulate a title retaining the N.B. initials of the parent company.

Working at Barrowden commenced in 1942, i.e. shortly after Nassington, but there had been proposals to work here for more than twenty years before. The earliest known reference is in the records of the Burghley estates, where G. Keeble is reported as making trial holes at Barrowden (in a letter dated 3rd April 1916); and GSM refers to 'arrangements recently (1918) made for working opencast on the northwest side of the Welland valley'. Clearly, nothing came of these proposals, probably because of the end of the war, and it was not until the advent of World War II that they were revived. NSI states that the new workings 'adjoin a trial gullet driven by J. Keeble' and we infer that all these early references are to one and the same place.

The quarries were on a bare spur of land, on both sides of the road from Morcott to Turtle Bridge over the Welland; and though the LMSR Rugby-Peterborough line lay a mere few hundred yards away from the working face, no connecting line was laid. Instead, lorries were used to convey the output nearly two miles to a tipping dock in the yard at Seaton station. Conditions in the pit were unusual, too, as NSI tells us that all operations — stripping topsoil, digging, loading into lorries and subsequent levelling and resoiling — were carried out by a single machine, a Ruston Bucyrus 3W dragline hired for the purpose. Loading into wagons at Seaton station was carried out by a Ransomes & Rapier 431 shovel, owned by the same company.

The quarries, locally called 'Red Hill'. were closed in 1948 and the worked land was efficiently restored to agriculture, the difference in level

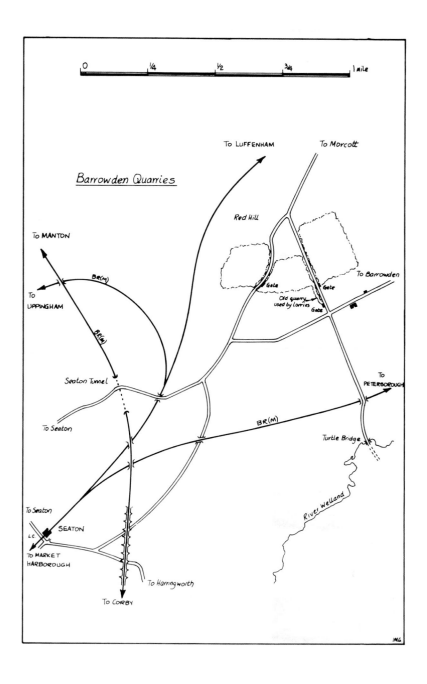

Barrowden Quarries

between road and fields being the only indication that minerals were recovered. This B672 road from Morcott to Caldicott runs south from the main Leicester-Uppingham road and then swings sharply west, but from the corner the old route continues as a 'grass road' (as the signposts put it) down to the curiously-named Turtle Bridge. There is no sign of ironstone working on this lower stretch. There is a minor road—little more than a bridleway—cutting across the ironstone area west of the B672 where it makes three sharp turns in less than a mile; this was probably the original route, as it is shorter, but was too steeply graded for general use. The OS 1:50000 first series shows this as a footpath for most of its length, but inspection of the site reveals that quarrying took place on both sides— on the east up to the B672, as we have noted, and west to the outcrop as the ground falls away. The eastern hedge has been replaced for part of its length, suggesting that quarrying stopped at the bridleway, while half way along a gap in the hedge was probably where lorries crossed the route. Just north of the right-angle bend in the B672 there are in both hedges very wide gates almost opposite each other, the gates supported on old sleepers; these were evidently exits for lorries. Keeble's gullet was on the west side of this road, but no separate traces of it remain.

Barrowden Quarry. Former quarrying area, with hedge of bridleway on right. 25th March 1981. (G. Kobish)

Grid References

926993	Gated exit from Quarries
922996	Road removed by quarrying

Quarry Machines

In Quarry

3W	D. Walking Dragline	RB				(a)	(1)

(a) hired from?   (1) returned to hirer

At Seaton Station for loading

431	D. Shovel	R&R	941	1939	(a)	(1)

(a) ex Nassington Quarries c 1942

(1) to Nassington Quarries c 1948

UPPINGHAM QUARRIES

Owners: James Pain Ltd

The quarries in the southern corner of Rutland—Uppingham, Pilton and Luffenham—were somewhat isolated from the main ironstone area and tended to be overlooked to some extent, hence our knowledge of them is not as complete as we would wish; this particularly applies to the Uppingham quarries, which had only a comparatively short and uneventful life. This system was one of the last to be developed by James Pain and was managed by his son Gordon. Details of the lease or purchase of land have not been discovered, but there were workings on each side of the Kettering road about half a mile south of Uppingham, which stands on a hill to the south and west of which the ground is much broken up into ridges and valleys by small tributaries of the Welland. The former LNWR branch followed the course of one such stream but for the last half mile before the terminus the line took to a side valley to reach the station; to do so it crossed the stream by a high bridge, and immediately east of this the Uppingham quarry line turned off and continued along the valley on the south side of the stream, starting off behind a grove of oak and birch. The siding agreement with the LNWR was dated 14th October 1912.

The first locomotive arrived in November 1912 and was presumably used in the construction of the line which, though only a simple one about three quarters of a mile in length, was steeply graded and called for more earthworks than usual. The *Kettering Leader* of 13th February 1914 reported that 'Messrs Pain Ltd will shortly have their pits at Uppingham in full swing' and that a tunnel was being constructed beneath the Kettering road. A 20-ton Ruston Proctor steam navvy had been supplied in January, and production at the Glebe quarry doubtless started very shortly afterwards, with the face stretching west from the main road to Gipsy Hollow Lane. At this time there was, as far as is known, only one locomotive, a Peckett 0-4-0 saddle tank, appropriately named *UPPINGHAM* on brass plates, and painted green lined black edged yellow. As the tramway had a ruling gradient of about 1 in 40 for the whole distance, *UPPINGHAM* shoving up the empties must have been plainly audible to boys of Uppingham School! The locomotive shed lay close to the LNWR junction, and just beyond it there was a passing loop to accommodate empty wagons; this loop crossed at right angles the course of an earlier narrow gauge incline from a clay pit to a small brickworks.

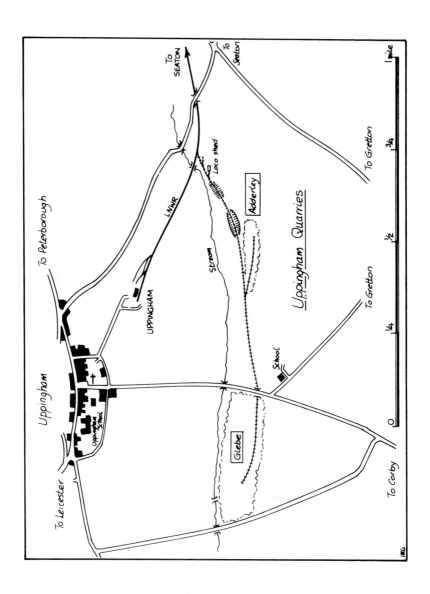

To meet increased wartime demand, a second quarry was opened, on the east side of the main road; known as Adderley quarry, it was reached by a branch making a trailing junction with the main tramway, and again was steeply graded. The little Peckett must have found it hard going, particularly holding the load on the bank down to the LNWR, and when the new quarry was opened two bigger locomotives were brought in; these were Avonside six-wheelers, one new (*UPPINGHAM*) and one transferred from Market Overton quarries and named *ADDERLEY*, probably after arrival here. The Peckett went to Market Overton, presumably about the same time. The new *UPPINGHAM* had a chocolate livery, later changed to green, and *ADDERLEY* was green, lined black edged white.

German prisoners-of-war worked in the quarries and were housed in huts alongside the Lyddington road, as recalled by Mr. R. Southwell, while in his letter of 9th November 1984 Mr. Hugh Reilly relates very vivid childhood recollections of seeing the prisoners 'pushing the trucks of stone under the road'. They were being pushed downhill, so perhaps *UPPINGHAM* merely brought up the empties, the full wagons being taken down at least part of the way manually, with the help of gravity. In his letter of 10th November

Uppingham Quarries. No photograph of the locomotives at work here have been discovered. Our picture of *UPPINGHAM* (P 1257) was taken at the Wirksworth quarries in Derbyshire on 25th April 1953. (J. R. Bonser)

1984 Mr. Southwell mentions 'wagons being loaded from wheelbarrows pushed over the wagons on planks'. The prisoners worked in both pits.

For a short time probably both pits were in use, working south from the outcrop; whether a machine was used in Adderley pit is uncertain, but it seems unlikely—GSM does not mention one, and the overburden was less. The reserves at Uppingham were not very large, as the ground falls away further to the west, but complete exploitation was never carried out. The Uppingham School authorities had consistently opposed the quarrying activities and, when the Armistice had cancelled the overriding demands for ore for military purposes, they purchased for playing fields the ground that Pain had hoped to lease. In the changed circumstances the company did not make any further attempts to acquire ground and there was a temporary closure in 1921; Mrs. E. R. Cross (in a letter dated 18th November 1984) recalled that one quarryman returned to the pit to collect his tools, and was killed by a runaway truck. Complete closure came about in 1926, probably at the start of the General Strike. The two locomotives apparently stood idle in the shed and then were moved to Market Overton for storage, and the track was lifted. When Stanton Ironworks Co Ltd took over Pain's business in 1928 nothing remained to be done but clearing up a few legal formalities. However, a plan preserved in Leicestershire Record Office, and deriving from British Steel Corporation sources, shows the potential ironstone areas to the west and south of Uppingham, with the implication that the United Steel Companies Ltd were interested in the possibility of development here, but nothing came of this.

There was no restoration of the ground and there are plenty of remains today. The course of the line can be followed from its junction with the BR trackbed, first embanked to make a wide ledge on the hillside to accommodate the double-track section, and then turning almost due west as a single line in shallow cutting almost to the top of the hill, from which the branch to Adderley pit is shown on the 6ins OS but not the course of the tramway, which is as clearly defined as the former BR branch; probably its significance was not realised.

The route towards Glebe pit is very heavily overgrown near the Kettering road; the east parapet of the bridge—of red brick capped with blue brick—remained until the early 1980s, though the west parapet was half demolished; the latter has been replaced by wooden boards, the east by a fence. Glebe pit, which was much the larger, remained as an open quarry for many years but in the 1970s was used as a dump for domestic refuse, and by 1979 was nearly completely filled—and so it remained in 1984, unused agriculturally and more of an eyesore than the old quarry; what Uppingham

Uppingham Quarries. The parapet of the tramway bridge under the Kettering road. This relic was demolished in the early 1980s. (G. Kobish)

School thought of the quarry in its wild and rubbish-filled state we have not enquired! The field along the north edge of this crudely-filled gullet is irregular and with small pools in wet weather, suggesting settling or imperfect levelling of the dumped overburden that drops away to a stream on the north side. Near the Gipsy Hollow Lane end is a curious survival — a flat-topped narrow embankment crossing the stream by a culvert, heading northwest; it has every appearance of being designed to carry a tramway, but whether it was used to dump waste from the Glebe pit or whether some quarrying took place on the north side of the stream is unknown. The embankment is well below the level of the quarry site now, but this may have been due to the dumping of overburden as working moved south. More than that we are unlikely to learn. Playing fields belonging to the School lie to the northeast, so possibly this was the area of Pain's thwarted intentions.

Grid References

877992	Locomotive shed
869989	Hilltop junction to Adderley Pit
873990	Adderley Pit
867989	Bridge under Kettering road
862989	Glebe Pit terminus
862991	Bridge over stream (embankment north of Glebe Pit)

Locomotives

Gauge; 4ft.8½in.

No. 1	UPPINGHAM	0-4-0ST	OC	P	1257	1912	12 x 18in.	3ft.0½in.	New 11/1912	(1)
	ADDERLEY	0-6-0ST	OC	AE	1694	1915	14 x 20in.	3ft.3in.	(a)	(2)
	UPPINGHAM	0-6-0ST	OC	AE	1806	1918	14 x 20in.	3ft.3in.	New 1918	(3)

(a) ex Market Overton Quarries c 1918

(1) to Market Overton Quarries
(2) to Market Overton Quarries c 1927
(3) to Market Overton Quarries by 7/1923; ex Mkt Overton by 2/1924; to Mkt Overton c 1927.

Quarry Machine

No. 20	S.Navvy. Rail		RP	423	1914	2¼ Cu.Yds.		30ft.	New 1/1914	(1)

(1) to Market Overton Quarries 1926

LUFFENHAM QUARRIES

Owners: Luffenham Iron Ore Co Ltd.

It is a curious fact that the histories of some of the smallest and shortest-lived quarry systems are the most difficult to unravel; possibly because they **were** small and thus received scant attention, or because they were imperfectly recorded. The latter shortcoming does not apply to Luffenham, about which a large amount of material exists in the Ancaster estate papers in the care of the Lincolnshire Record Office; meticulous extracts have been made from these by Roger West, to whom we are greatly indebted. Even so, much of this material is concerned with trivia-minor events of a day-to-day nature that happens in any firm and is really of more interest to a sociologist trying to picture a way of life in the 1920s than to an historian concerned with broader issues. Nevertheless, there is a great deal of information in these files, without which our knowledge of the company would be very much the poorer.

The Luffenham Iron Ore Co Ltd was promoted by the Kettering Iron & Coal Co Ltd, but as an associated company rather than a subsidiary, with a number of directors common to both boards. The object of KICC was to ensure continuity of supply of limestone, as their existing source — Barlow's quarries at Finedon — was becoming exhausted, and in November 1917 the KICC board agreed to purchase the freehold of the 28 acres of the Edith Weston stone quarries, which had not been used since 1914 (see board minutes 27th November 1917). It was considered that the new site could best be administered by a new company, 'the primary object of which was the acquisition of these quarries and of limestone and ironstone in adjoining lands of Lord Ancaster and others' (board minutes 10th January 1919). Mr. G. H. Johnson, a KICC director, stated in a letter of 24th April 1963 that the company had been formed to work ironstone on the evidence of an outcrop in a shallow railway cutting three quarters of a mile east of Luffenham station, and close to Foster's Bridge over the river Chater; but it seems clear from the above that the working of ironstone was of minor importance, and after all KICC could have had little need to bring in iron ore from elsewhere.

Two leases were negotiated with the Earl of Ancaster, both dated 6th April 1919. No. 1 comprised 170 acres in South Luffenham for a period of thirty years; No. 2 consisted of 1577 acres in the parishes of Edith Weston, Normanton and North Luffenham, plus six acres for sidings at the Midland

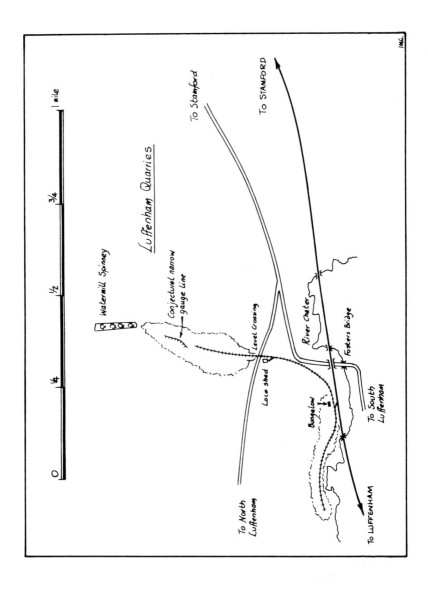

Luffenham Quarries

Watermill Spinney

Conjectural narrow gauge line

Level Crossing

Loco Shed

Bungalow

River Chater

Foxters Bridge

To Stamford

To STAMFORD

To North Luffenham

To South Luffenham

To LUFFENHAM

1 mile

¾   ½   ¼   0

Railway, and was for a period of 50 years. Royalties were set at 8d per ton for ironstone (or 2d, according to the overburden), 2½d for limestone and other minerals, and a wayleave of 1/2d per ton.

Operations commenced in 1919; KICC supplied a navvy in August 1919, and a locomotive at Foster's Bridge sidings. It seems, however, that the first area to be worked was not that adjacent to Foster's Bridge (the remains of which are still visible) but at the Edith Weston quarries about a mile and a half to the north; LQ for 1920 (there is no issue for 1919) records under Luffenham Iron Co Ltd only Edith Weston, with Henry King as manager, as he had been in the time of the previous owners, Edith Weston Freestone Co. The next issue of LQ, 1922, quotes Foster's Bridge, Luffenham Siding and North and South Luffenham quarries. Transport between Edith Weston and Foster's Bridge siding was by steam lorry. There is a story that German prisoners-of-war were set to dig a cutting from Foster's Bridge to Edith Weston for a tramway connection between the two; but the war ended very soon after, the prisoners were repatriated, and the cutting was abandoned (see *The Lincolnshire Limestone*—Jeffrey A. Best, Susan Parker and Christine D. Mitchell; Nene Valley College, Northampton, 1978). By the beginning of 1920 the quarries at Foster's Bridge and at Luffenham Siding had commenced production, mostly of limestone for Kettering furnaces and elsewhere, and a trifling quantity of ironstone. NSI records ironstone for 1920/1, but afterwards limestone only; it seems that the disturbed nature of the ground made quarrying difficult for the plant on the site.

Little information is available for the period 1921-23 but two machines were being used, one with a long jib and another with a short jib, and output seems to have been rather erratic, with ironstone still forming only a very small part. The tramway was a simple standard gauge affair with a few sidings on the north side of the MR line and a single track curving away northwards from the eastern end, crossing the lane to North Luffenham on the level on its way to the quarry on the north side. The level crossing gates were double, rather surprisingly for such a small system, and adjacent to them on the south side were the office and the locomotive shed of corrugated iron with one 'pot'. The occupant of the shed is the subject of some mystery; the only known locomotive is Manning wardle 1286, which was No. 9 in KICC stock. She was certainly there from 1924 onwards, and was probably the locomotive sent to Luffenham in 1919, but this requires confirmation. KICC Engine Repair records (copied out by Ken Plant, to whom we are indebted) contains references to boiler inspections in 1919/20 and repairs in 1922, but these could have been carried out when the engine was at Luffenham, as she was still KICC property. We must leave the identity of the 1919 locomotive at Foster's Bridge as a query and pass on to another curious point, the name carried by MW 1286. She is quoted as being named *CARRINGTON* at Kettering, and Eddy Stafford, the driver at Luffenham, says the plates with this name were lying in the shed at Luffenham after the title on the tank had been changed to *THE LUFFENHAM IRON CO LTD*; these were on brass plates, as borne out by a photograph loaned to us by Horace, Eddy's brother-in-law, who also supplied this information. However, Frank Jones has a photograph of the locomotive in its pre-Kettering day on contracting work for Holme & King, and bearing the name *CARINGTON*. The Engine Repair records of KICC for 25th November 1915 say about locomotive No. 9 'Two new nameplates on tank'. The new plates could well have had the double 'R' — by design or phonetic accident with the short 'A' and single 'R' converted to the double 'R'. No one seems to be able to say categorically that the new plates had the double 'R', but they appear to think so; and, who knows?, the plates might still be on the shed site buried in the ground.

The north end of the Foster's Bridge quarry was at a higher level than the main section and here was laid a three-foot gauge tramway; this was only a very short line, but the very small locomotive *YUM YUM* was transferred from Kettering to work it, and by a stroke of good fortune a photograph in

Luffenham Quarries. *CARINGTON* on contracting work before coming to Luffenham. See text for discussion on the name. (Collection F. Jones)

Luffenham Quarries. The limestone quarry with two Ruston 20 ton navvies. The upper one (RH 533) is fitted with a long jib for removing overburden, the lower one (RH 650) loading wagons in the charge of the Manning Wardle locomotive. At the rear can be seen the 3ft. gauge line with *YUM YUM* in steam; this is on a higher level. 1924.

(Ruston & Hornsby)

the Ruston & Hornsby files shows both the narrow and standard gauge locomotives at work with the two navvies; the short jib machine loading and the long jib machine dealing with the overburden. Until the photograph came to light the existence of narrow gauge here was unsuspected but the presence of *YUM YUM* is confirmed in the Ancaster papers. If we accept the story of the German POWs digging a cutting here, it is reasonable to suppose that the three-foot tramway was laid along it and also that the original intention was to lay a three-foot tramway to Edith Weston after the fashion of the Kettering quarry system. The narrow gauge tramway was short-lived, however, and *YUM YUM* was returned to Kettering later in the same year, 1924.

A small amount of ironstone was quarried in 1924/5, according to Ancaster estate records, but was not expected to last long as it was found to be of poor quality; the customer was Partington Iron & Steel Co Ltd of Irlam, who nevertheless seem to have been satisfied — the last recorded delivery was on 9th June 1925, but as late as October 1926 they were enquiring about further supplies, only to be told that 'none was being mined now'. Production of limestone continued but even that brought in many complaints, and in 1927 the company changed its title to the Luffenham Stone & Asphalt Co Ltd in conformity with their new business associated with roadmaking. Stone obtained from the quarries, including Edith Weston, was ground and mixed with asphalt for this purpose. A tarmac plant was constructed on the south side of the LMSR line a little nearer Luffenham station and supplies for this were brought in from the quarry by lorry from Foster's Bridge and mixed with ironworks slag coming in by rail. These operations were scarcely more successful and came to an end on 22nd December 1930, when the plant was abruptly shut down.

Of the two diggers, the long jib one had already been sold in 1929, and the short jib one was now sold to a dealer but later returned to ironstone service at Glendon. The latter-day history of the locomotive is less precisely known; she is believed to have been acquired by Ancaster Estates in lieu of payment because of the bankruptcy of the company. She was left in the shed just as she was at the end of the day's work, with water in the boiler and tank, and ashes in the grate; the resultant heavy corrosion rendered her unacceptable to the engineer of Pilton Ironstone Co when he came on a visit of inspection some eight years later. Tom Hodson of KICC said that she was purchased by J. Standen of Peterborough from Ancaster Estate, and possibly it was he who engineered the abortive attempt to sell her to Pilton. Eventually the locomotive was sold to A. R. Adams of Newport and later did service at Royal Ordnance Factories at Ranskill and

Maltby. The tarmac plant was sold to Tarmac Ltd and dismantled early in 1931. The rails were taken up, otherwise the system was just left to rusticate, including the double level-crossing gates and the locomotive shed alongside. The quarries themselves were given over to a wild profusion of limestone-loving plants such as Vipers Bugloss and Chicory.

The quarry was reopened, in the later 1960s it is believed, for road-filling material, transport being by lorry on concrete roads. The shed was used first for storing farm implements and later as a private garage, with window spaces covered by corrugated iron or its plastics-age equivalent, polythene; the 'pot' was still in position and the whole building looked pretty delapidated. It was demolished in the early 1970s, when also the Post Office erected a building on the north side of the level crossing. The gates went about 1960. The quarry area close to the BR line between Luffenham station and Foster's Bridge was still extant though overgrown up to 1984, when the middle section was 'landscaped' but the rest unaltered; the tramway course was used as access to a bungalow that had been built in the old quarry area—a nice sunny spot sheltered from the north winds by the quarry wall. The principal quarry north of the level crossing is still in the rough state as left by the quarry operator and others that have entered the site, and the floor at the northern end is at the higher level used by the narrow gauge line, and exhibits a limestone face.

Luffenham Quarries. The locomotive shed by the level crossing, 24th October 1968. *CARINGTON* resided here out of use, from 1930 to 1936; the building itself remained until the early 1970s.   (J. R. Bonser)

Grid References

958032	Quarry terminus by BR
961033	Level crossing/locomotive shed
952028(?)	Tarmac plant
962039	End of gullet above level crossing
965056	Edith Weston Quarry

Locomotives

Gauge; 4ft. 8½in.

(CARRINGTON)	0-6-0ST	OC	MW	1286	1894	15 x 20in.	3ft.1in.	(a)	(1)

(a) ex Kettering Iron & Coal Co Ltd, 1919. See text for discussion of name

(1) to A. R. Adams Ltd, Newport, Mon.; to R.O.F. Ranskill, Nottinghamshire 1937

Gauge; 3ft.0in.

YUM YUM	0-4-0ST	OC	BH	893	1887	6 x 10in.	2ft.0in.	(a)	(1)

(a) ex Kettering Quarries c 5/1924

(1) to Kettering Quarries 10/1924

Quarry Machines

No. 20	S.Navvy. Long Jib	RH	533	1919		55ft.	New 8/1919	(1)
No. 20	S. Shovel	RH	650	1921	3 Cu.Yds.	31ft.	New 1/1921	(2)

(1) to Thos. W. Ward Ltd 5/1929
(2) to F. Edmunds, dealer, Barlaston, Staffordshire; then to Glendon Quarries 6/1930

PILTON QUARRIES

Owners: Pilton Ironstone Co; Staveley Coal & Iron Co Ltd (Pilton Ironstone Dept) from c. 1933: Staveley Iron & Chemical Co Ltd from 23rd September 1948; Staveley Minerals Ltd from 7th March 1961.

It was the policy of the Staveley Coal & Iron Co Ltd to operate their ironstone quarries through subsidiary companies, sometimes jointly with other ironmasters; this system was adhered to after World War I but the existence of a single controlling body was apparent in the high degree of standardisation of equipment. On the locomotive side, for example, each of the standard gauge systems (Pitsford, Lamport, Cranford, Pilton) had one of the big and handsome six-coupled Avonside saddle tanks; on the other hand, transfers of locomotives between quarries were few compared with Stanton quarries. This arose from the policy of repairing locomotives at their own sheds, whereas Stanton locomotives went to Holwell or Stanton ironworks for heavy overhaul. The Staveley systems also showed a marked similarity in the type of building used, including locomotive sheds and workshops of corrugated iron, painted maroon (in later years, green), sometimes with brick walls and iron-framed windows.

Pilton quarries lay between the villages of Luffenham and Wing in southeast Rutland, on a ridge of high ground paralleling the Midland Railway Manton—Peterborough line, here following the valley of the river Chater. It was originally intended that the company title should be Luffenham Ironstone Co, which was used in the initial negotiations, recorded in the Staveley board minutes as far back as January 1914; but this was abandoned in favour of the Pilton title when it was realised that confusion could obviously arise (e.g. in wagon consignment) with the Luffenham Iron Ore Co Ltd, which started operations about the same time and which had prior claim to the title. A rubber stamp 'Luffenham Ironstone Company' survived at Pilton until 1954, and the surveyors' plans are titled 'Luffenham Quarries'.

The largest quarrying area of some 300 acres between the Pilton-Morcott and Luffenham-Morcott roads was purchased from Ancaster Estates, while east of the Pilton-Morcott road a smaller area was leased from Mr. C. H. Wood. It appears that the original intention was to instal a narrow gauge tramway — probably of 3ft or metre gauge — from the quarries to a tipping dock at the MR sidings, as in the BSC archives there is a surveyor's plan showing the proposed layout at the exchange point. In the event, a

Pilton Quarries. Excavation of the cutting in 1919 from the road bridge to Robinson's End, with Bagnall locomotive *PIXIE* and the No. 5 steam shovel loading 2ft. gauge wagons. Just above the navvy jib can be seen the roadside wooden huts used by the contractor's men. These huts remained afterwards.

(Ruston & Hornsby; Courtesy of Bert Smith)

standard gauge tramway was chosen instead, in line with contemporary developments at Staveley's quarries in Northamptonshire—Pitsford (a new system, like Pilton) and Cranford (where the metre gauge was being replaced by standard gauge). However, a narrow gauge tramway was used in the constructional work.

The *Kettering Leader* of 13th February 1919 reports 'Staveley are about to open a pit at Pilton'; there was a considerable amount of earth moving to be done in excavating cuttings on the higher ground and building up the embanked formation of the standard gauge line down to the MR sidings, and for this purpose a two-foot gauge tramway was provided, a method that had been used at Eastwell quarries. This was worked by two steam locomotives—the Orenstein & Koppel *KEIGHLEY* from Eastwell and the much better known *PIXIE* that came here new, a standard Bagnall contractor's locomotive that in later years performed 'ganistering' at Cranford and became one of the earliest candidates for preservation. A third locomotive, *DEFIANCE*, has been mentioned, but no details are known and she may have been hired from a contractor. *PIXIE* was here for four years, in which time the narrow gauge was extended about three quarters of a mile to Pilton village in the course of excavating the cutting to Scott's pit. The narrow gauge crossed 'Green Lane' by a bridge and then ran to a gantry over the standard gauge so that the loaded steel side-tipping wagons could be emptied into railway wagons below. These side-tippers were of standard design, and bodies of several of them remained for many years at the locomotive shed. There was also a bogie wagon (ex War Department) for carrying coal, as used at Loddington, Eastwell etc. *PIXIE* worked in conjunction with a Ruston No. 5 steam shovel, as shown in the interesting Ruston & Hornsby photograph in the possession of Bert Smith. In the course of excavation the ironstone outcrop was reached west of the administrative area, and the surveyor's plan records that working commenced in August 1920, with the ore evidently despatched by a combination of narrow and standard gauge tramways.

PIXIE returned in 1928 but was transferred in the same year to the Basic quarries at Eaton in Leicestershire. The reason for her return to Pilton is not remembered, but an interesting possibility is suggested by a proposed branch included on a survey map in the BSC archives. This shows the course of a line at a lower level than the original, leaving the main tramway immediately south of the exchange sidings and running along the flank of the hill due west, under the road to Lyndon and then heading towards the area of Wing quarries. There is no indication that this line was ever started, but it could have been the intention to use *PIXIE* on constructional work in

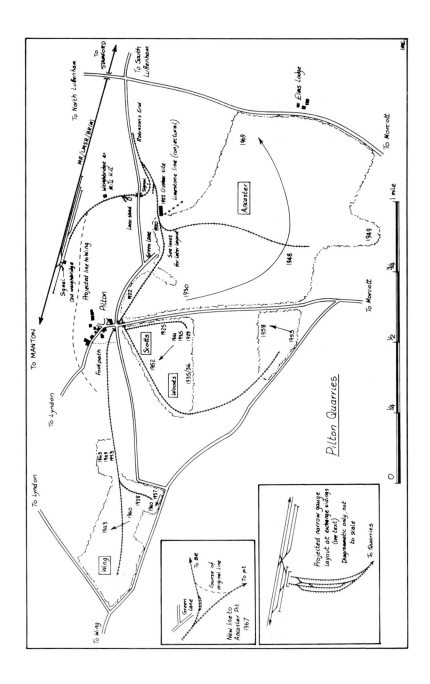

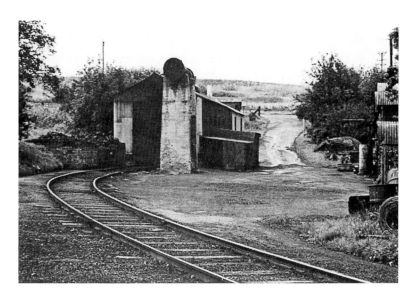

Pilton Quarries. Locomotive shed, 8th June 1967. The shed appears to have been extended rearwards at some time. Note water tank, left, stores and workshops, right. Line to quarries ran to left of the trees. (M. J. Leah)

the same way that the narrow gauge had been used to open up the line to Pilton, by this time in use for traffic. The date is perhaps significant; with reduced demand, plans to open the quarries at Wing would be shelved, and *PIXIE* sent away again, never to return. When Wing pit was opened some years later, an entirely different route was selected.

Leaving these speculations for the realities, the standard gauge tramway was interesting enough, starting from the LMSR sidings and climbing the hillside on a low embankment on a curve at a gradient of about 1 in 25 to the headquarters north of the Pilton-South Luffenham road. Here were the office, locomotive shed and workshops. Maroon-painted corrugated iron seemed to be the predominant building material, but some brick and wood were used as well. The weigh cabin of brick was down at the marshalling sidings. Beyond the locomotive shed (which held three locos) the line plunged immediately into deep cutting under the road, carried over by an unusually fine bridge of red and blue brick with parapets including some ironwork; the line swung sharply eastwards, still on a rising gradient, parallel with the road to a reversing point with storage sidings known as Robinson's End, from the name of the occupier of the adjoining land. The line to the quarries then ran westwards more or less on the level, with a passing loop and on the south side a high concrete wall that was at one time used as a tipping dock, with high ground on the south side. A short way beyond this point the line divided, that to Ancaster pit turning due south and crossing Green Lane en route; the other branch also crossed Green Lane and then followed the line of the road, but in deep cutting, to the crossroads of the tiny village of Pilton, where the line forked again. The left hand track passed under the Pilton-Morcott road by a concrete bridge and swung south to Scott's pit; the right hand line passed right under the crossroads by a longer tunnel — with refuges in the concrete walls on each side — to emerge on the northwest side and then run a further three quarters of a mile to Wing pit. These two bridges side by side made a feature unique to Pilton and gave the impression of a main line railway, heightened by the chaired track on wooden sleepers. The chaired track ran from the quarries to Robinson's End, while from the latter to the LMSR sidings the track was flat-bottomed, an unusual combination.

The line also boasted two signals. The approach to the office area from Robinson's End was hidden by the cutting, and the curve of the line by the

Pilton Quarries. The signal was installed because of the sharp curve in deep cutting approaching the yard. Latterly it was unused. 10th April 1967. (J. R. Bonser)

Pilton Quarries. *STAMFORD* brings the last load of ore from the quarries to the exchange sidings on 4th June 1969. The original weigh house is at left. At right is the swing signal, indicating to the driver of the BR locomotive that the siding is occupied.   (G. H. Starmer)

overbridge, all heavily embowered with trees; a semaphore signal supplied by Westinghouse Brake & Signal Co Ltd, complete with spectacles, lamp, compensating weights and finial, and operated from the office, was placed along this section. The entrance to the marshalling yard by the Stamford line was protected by a signal of the centrally-pivoted board type, that in the 'on' position projected across the track and was knocked into the 'off' position parallel to the railway when a train passed, thus indicating to the next driver that the section was occupied. This signal was erected by the LMSR. Both signals were largely disused in later years, when only one locomotive was normally in steam.

Production at Ancaster pit east of the Pilton-Morcott road commenced in 1922 at the northern perimeter, parallel to the Pilton-Luffenham road, and working was anti-clockwise right up to the final closure, when the face was practically in line (NNW-ESE) with the first cut, having moved round 180 degrees. Scott's pit (sometimes called Wood's pit, as part of the ground had been leased from C. H. Wood) west of the Pilton-Morcott road was opened in 1924 and production here was carried on up to 1929, when a break occurred, and was resumed briefly in 1935/6, then from 1941 to 1952, working clockwise. The line to Wing pit was apparently laid down in the middle 1930s, with production commencing in 1937, as an alternative to Scott's pit; but during the World War II period all three pits were in production. Calcining was introduced (possibly from the start in pit

35

Pilton Quarries. Ancaster pit, May 1949, with 30-ton shovel (RH 640) working with the 1940 Stothert & Pitt transporter. The latter was the last transporter supplied to the ironstone industry. The machine at the top of the face is a drill.   (BGS)

bottoms) and in the war years at clamps alongside the LMSR sidings; some calcining was also carried out on the floor of Ancaster pit during World War II, when most of the output was calcined. By this time the layout of the Pilton system was essentially complete, and very picturesque it was; the line from the shed area ran through a wooded cutting, then to Robinson's End behind a grove of poplars. The line to Ancaster pit was more open and on the south side was the concrete tipping dock that had been used in the 1920s; limestone from Ancaster pit was taken up in wooden side-tipping wagons (of which there were about twenty) and tipped via a 'cracker' (crusher) into railway wagons below. The same type of 'Ship Canal' wagons were used to carry ironstone to the calcine clamps, but later (about 1940) standard steel 'dumpcars' were introduced. The branch to Scott's and Wing pits was in cutting most of the way, and was a delightful setting for the well-kept locomotives. Scott's pit started immediately beyond the bridge under the Morcott road, but later the line was extended some three quarters of a mile to a new quarry further south. Wing pit was a similar distance from the bridge under the crossroads, beyond which the line passed through an orchard and over a level crossing with a farm track before taking to the open fields; the quarrying area lay beyond the 'kink' in the road to Wing.

Pilton Quarries. Ruston No. 20 steam shovel, RH 780 at Scott's pit. c 1935. (Collection Marshall Fayers)

Steam excavating machinery was introduced at the outset — four new Ruston & Hornsby diggers and a transporter purchased in 1924. The 20-ton shovel on caterpillar tracks worked in Scott's pit, the others in Ancaster, where an overburden up to 35 feet had to be dealt with. At Wing pit the stone was under thin cover. Two more shovels were obtained secondhand in the 1930s and were used in Scott's pit, the 10-ton machine being used to load calcined ore. Pilton was amongst the last ironstone quarries to use steam quarry machinery — until the late 1950s — and is also believed to be the very last one to employ a transporter; this was a machine supplied by Stothert & Pitt Ltd of Bath as late as 1940, and it was said that other builders declined to quote for what they thought an old-fashioned machine, offering instead standard draglines. This transporter was scrapped in 1961, following the last Ruston navvy (No. 640) that had worked with it. Two 43RB diesels, a dragline and a shovel, came in 1940 and were used in Wing pit at first, and an oil supply for them was installed by the double bridge. The steam equipment was cut up just beyond this bridge. The 'barrow and plank' system of overburden disposal, termed 'top-road running' at Pilton, lasted here as late as 1939. Another anachronism was provided by the spares service for excavators; these were carried to the machines by pony and trap well into the motor age. The pony finished her days on a milk round in Market Harborough.

Working at Wing pit was clockwise from south to north, followed by a small quarry further east, towards Pilton; production was heavy throughout most of the war but came to an end in 1944; there was a small but brief revival in 1953, and that was all. The Pilton quarries as a group however seem not to have suffered much cutback at the end of the war. Ancaster pit was extended in 1948, the face being swung round from the Morcott road direction. The original Scott's pit continued in production up to 1952, and a new face about half a mile south, on the west side of the Morcott road, was opened up and worked 1953-58, using a 5W diesel-electric walking dragline, probably with a 43RB for loading; the tramway was extended in an arc, with a passing loop en route to reach it. This area was part of a lease of 40 acres, and the rest was never worked, all production from 1958 onwards coming from Ancaster; here, electric equipment was used, including a 5W walking dragline and a 54RB shovel.[1] Lifting of track at Wing pit took place in the early 1950s, when the earlier quarrying area was restored—the western part to grass, the eastern part to conifers, and the tramway route filled with rubbish; the track was complete as far as the occupation crossing in Pilton but mostly buried beyond, the latter section being lifted in 1965. Track to Scott's pit was lifted soon after production ceased.

The locomotive stock at Pilton was remarkably constant, with locomotives purchased new at intervals and three others obtained secondhand for shorter periods, all six-coupled saddle tanks. The first was an Avonside appropriately named *PILTON* though the initial correspondence with the makers was undertaken under the company's provisional title of Luffenham Ironstone Co; but there is no suggestion that the name originally selected was *LUFFENHAM*. She had a livery of green lined black edged white, with the name on brass plates on the tank. When production commenced she was joined by *IRENE*, a Manning Wardle transferred from Midland Ironstone Co Ltd (another Staveley subsidiary) of Crosby, near Scunthorpe; she later went to Pitsford. Another Avonside came in 1927, by which time Scott's pit had been opened up; named *STAMFORD*, she was similar in mechanical dimensions and livery to *PILTON*, but differed externally in a number of respects. The most striking was the cab, rounded at the roof instead of being angled, and open-backed instead of closed; this was so that she could safely negotiate the narrow tunnel on the Cranford line, and thus deputise for *CRANFORD* when the latter was under repair—which she did on one occasion. *STAMFORD* also had angled spectacles instead of round, and a different type of dome and safety valve. *PILTON* had dumb (wooden) buffers for handling the wooden side-tippers; *STAMFORD* had a block on the bufferbeam instead.

The opening of Wing pit called for a third locomotive, and the purchase

Pilton Quarries. Avonside locomotive *PILTON* in the shed yard 4th September 1947. The hutments can be glimpsed at left (see photo of *PIXIE*). Note wooden buffers for dealing with the wooden side-tipping wagons.
(G. Alliez. Courtesy of B. D. Stoyel)

of the disused locomotive lying at Luffenham quarries was considered; but she was found to be too badly gone, and a new Bagnall was obtained. This was the first of a standard series of Bagnall locomotives supplied during the war for ironstone traffic and was painted green, lined black edged red (inside) and yellow (outside) and named *STAVELEY* on brass plates; other locomotives of this class were generally named after the quarries concerned, on which basis this would have been *PILTON No. 2,* but possibly this locomotive was acquired as a general spare. Later in the war (she had gone by October 1943) she was sent to Midland Ironstone, while their *JULIA SHEFFIELD* was undergoing heavy repair, and was itself replaced by a museum piece weather-boarded Manning Wardle, *SIR BERKELEY,* in a livery of green, lined black edged white. The nameplates *SIR BERKELEY* had come off another locomotive (Manning Wardle 1631) at Midland Ironstone. Apart from a brief loan of *CRANFORD No. 2* in 1946, this completed the standard gauge locomotive stock, and from then onwards until the closure all traffic was handled by the three locomotives *PILTON, STAMFORD* and *STAVELEY.*

Pilton Quarries. Avonside locomotive *STAMFORD* at the exchange sidings. The photograph shows well the open-backed cab, so that the loco. could be sent if required to Cranford, where there was a very narrow tunnel, a derailment in which would otherwise trap the crew. Note the polished brass chimney cap and safety valve cover. 5th August 1936.

(G. Alliez. Courtesy of B. B. Stoyel)

Pilton Quarries. *STAVELEY* was the first of the series of locomotives built under Ministry of Supply authority by W. G. Bagnall for work in Staveley ironstone quarries in World War II. The picture shows her on one of the comparatively few occasions when she was working; she seems to have been an unpopular engine at Pilton. September 1963.

(K. Cooper/IRS Collection)

Concentration of production at the one working face led to simpler operating, with only one locomotive required in steam. The standard load was eight wagons, full or empty, with the locomotive pushing up the incline from the exchange sidings; there was a loop at the entrance to the quarry where the empties were left while the locomotive picked up the loaded wagons from the working face, then taking the empties forward

Pilton Quarries. Weigh Office by the side of the trackbed, looking towards the BR line, 26th April 1986. This building was brought from Mill Hill quarries in 1965. (A. J. Cocklin)

again. There used to be a passing loop near the tipping dock, but one connection was taken out — in the early 1960s, it is believed. Some fresh equipment arrived in the summer of 1965 from the recently-closed Mill Hill quarry near Eaton; this included a weighbridge and weighhouse, that were installed just below the office area, the main line being realigned to avoid any break in production. The old weighbridge down by the BR sidings was then abandoned. Some rail also arrived from Mill Hill and in 1966 this was utilised, along with rail from Lamport, and sections of track from the branch to Scott's and Wing pits, to reorganise the layout at Ancaster pit, the entrance to which was on a very tight curve. This was eased by putting in a reversing point, with a headshunt along the line towards Pilton (the rest of the branch being lifted), and the new line more or less along the site of Green Lane; at the same time the quarry line was relaid on top of the ironstone, with the loading machine on the quarry floor. This was in accordance with the practice of Stewarts & Lloyds Minerals Ltd, who had assumed complete control of Staveley Minerals Ltd from October 1965.

The new layout, while easing operations in some respects, still called for rather complicated locomotive manouevres, with empties left in the loop near the new reversing point while the locomotive fetched full wagons from the quarry; it then took the empties to the face and returned to propel the full wagons up to Robinson's End. A curious point is that while most of the track, including that in the quarry, was chaired, the 'straight through' line of the loop was flat-bottomed; this no doubt arose from the mixed bag of track available for the job. It seems that this routine was later simplified, the empties being left in the headshunt while the locomotive retrieved the full wagons, and the loop was disused. As some propelling of wagons was required, a warning system as used on Stewarts & Lloyds Minerals systems was introduced; an electric hooter giving a high-pitched and very far-reaching warbling note, was placed on the leading wagon.

The locomotive history of the post-World War II years is simple; apart from the brief loan of *STAVELEY* to Desborough, there were no stock changes and the same three locomotives carried on to the end. The newest locomotive, *STAVELEY*, never seems to have been popular at Pilton and when operations were restricted to Ancaster Pit and the use of one locomotive only, one of the Avonsides was preferred. *STAVELEY* is not know to have been used after 1958, and a year or so later was withdrawn with a defective firebox; she was moved around the premises from time to time, sometimes in the shed, sometimes on the siding by the tipping dock, but eventually finished up at the back of the shed, her original livery (she was never repainted) rusty and the tank encrusted with bird-droppings.

Pilton Quarries. *STAMFORD* pushes loaded tipplers through heavy rain to Robinson's End. From the latter point the locomotive would be at the head of the train for the downhill run to the sidings. 10th April 1967. (J. R. Bonser)

The traffic was worked by the Avonsides, each working usually for a long spell rather than both alternately; *PILTON* had a new boiler in 1958 and worked until late 1962, while *STAMFORD* received a new firebox. *STAMFORD* then took over up to the Spring of 1968; *PILTON* worked occasionally as a spare or on ballasting work. *PILTON* then worked the traffic to September 1968, with *STAMFORD* performing the concluding work. Both were repainted in the 1950s in the then standard Staveley Minerals livery of plain mid-green with red coupling rods. When Stewarts & Lloyds Minerals assumed control, plant numbers were allocated in the usual way: 8310/22-*PILTON*, 8310/23-*STAVELEY*, and 8310/24-*STAMFORD*.

When calcining ceased (in the late 1950s, it is believed) the ore was loaded into standard 27-ton tipplers at the quarry face. The steel dumpcars were left on a siding by the BR yard and some were there as late as 1968. Of the earlier wooden side-tippers, some twenty remained in 1954, but only three survived in 1965, in the siding by the tipping dock. Also still around at this time were the frame and wheels of a 2ft gauge side-tipper, along with two bodies, which were all at Scott's pit.

There was one enthusiast's 'Railtour' of the Pilton system, arranged by the genial manager, George Skelhon, for the Birmingham Locomotive Club on Saturday 21st May 1966, when *STAMFORD* was specially

Pilton Quarries. Birmingham Locomotive Club railtour of Pilton quarries. 21st May 1966, with *STAMFORD* taking the train up to Robinson's End. (J. M. Mason)

cleaned up at the head of a rake of six open wagons hired from BR. It was a beautiful sunny Spring Day (in more than twenty visits the author has yet to visit Pilton in inclement weather) and a grand time was had by all; photographers obtaining fine shots of locomotive working against a scenic background, the sound recordists doing equally well with the locomotive exhaust on the bank, and others just content to go along for the ride in congenial company. What a happy day it was.

The revised layout did not see a great deal of use; by the middle of 1967 output was down to 1000-1500 tons per week, equivalent to two or three day's work, so that the quarry only operated for the first half of the week. At this time the output went mostly to Corby, but twelve months later — mid 1968 — about 1500 tons per week were being sent to Tees-side; when demand was reduced at the end of 1968 while a furnace was under repair, Pilton was closed for ten weeks, the men meanwhile working at Corby quarries. Under these conditions, which obtained at so many ironstone quarries at the time, it was no surprise to learn of threatened closure. There had been rumours of this as early as February 1968, but no definite moves in this direction had been made and in fact Pilton was included in the plans for a far-reaching redistribution of motive power, details of which were circulated to quarry managers in a Memorandum dated 22nd October 1968. This arose from the purchase from BR at that time of 22 class 14 0-6-0 diesel hydraulic locomotives (D 95XX) which were earmarked for the major quarries at Corby, Glendon, Buckminster and Harlaxton; it was anticipated that they would release four ex-Oxfordshire Ironstone Sentinel 0-4-0 diesels (one from Glendon and three from North of the Welland) and one of each would be sent to Storefield, Irchester, Cranford and Pilton, with the relegation of steam to standby status at each of these places. The D 95XX arrived but the movement of the Sentinels was only partly implemented, forestalled by closure preparations at Cranford and Pilton.

Pilton had always been a well-kept, neat little system, but now things were allowed to slide; the buildings showed signs of needing attention, and repair work was cut. A tenant farmer accustomed to getting machinery repaired at the quarry workshops found it was no longer possible to get the work done here, as the power had been cut off. And so the sad tale unfolded in the familiar manner. The official date for the cessation of production was 7th June 1969; but, as the quarry was still working well below capacity, the last five wagons were loaded during the morning of 4th June (Wednesday) and taken down to the reception sidings. To emphasise that this was really the end, the electric face shovel was already on its way out of the pit in the afternoon, as far as the connecting cable allowed. The locomotive returned to the pit to help pull the cable along to the next junction box, but there was no electrician to connect it up — so *STAMFORD* returned to the shed for the last time, and the driver locked up. These sad proceedings were watched by a handful of enthusiasts keen to record the last rites.

Track lifting commenced immediately, but rail haulage was not used; sections of track were lifted to the top of the pit and loaded into a road trailer for despatch. By the end of August all the track had gone save for a section between the loco. shed and the upper signal; two months later all that remained was the short length outside the shed, wherein the three locomotives stood, gathering rust, dust and bird-droppings — a scene enacted in hundreds of places up and down the country in the middle of the twentieth century, but never losing its poignancy. The last working locomotive, *STAMFORD*, was reserved for preservation by the Bluebell Railway in Sussex, an unlikely destination — this being a purely passenger line — and little attention has been paid to her since. *PILTON* and *STAVELEY* left in November for Cohen's yard near Kettering, where *PILTON* is known to have been cut up in a matter of days, and probably *STAVELEY* in a few days more.

The remains at Pilton are a composite of complete obliteration and piecemeal degeneration. Initially the lower section from the BR sidings to south of the bridge under the Luffenham road was left intact apart from removal of track; beyond this the quarrying area was smoothed over and landscaped by earth-movers to a full return to agricultural use, with the exception of the last 200 yards or so of Ancaster pit, which was left open, ironstone 'bench' included. The buildings grouped round the yard were left standing, including the workshops, locomotive shed, water tank and weigh cabin (the ex-Mill Hill one). The loco. shed was purchased by the Peterborough Railway Society and taken away in December 1970 to the yard at Peterborough East station, where the Society had storage space; when the station was closed, the shed was moved with other items to the premises at Wansford station for erection there. The shed area at Pilton was used as a piggery and was still so in 1977, though by then the cottage nearby was abandoned and the workshops were very delapidated. The weigh cabin was still (1979) in fair condition, glass excepted, and the course of the line down to BR clear but overgrown, even some sleepers being present and the post of the rotary signal.

The bridge by the shed area is of red brick with three rows of blue brick and parapet ironwork of five sets of narrow gauge rails on each side; the cutting below is waterlogged. Only the first couple of hundred yards or so of 'Green Lane' remains, with beside it the electricity substation that was used for

Pilton Quarries. The famous twin tunnels under the Pilton crossroads. Tunnel to Scott's pit to the left, to Wing pit to right. Note signpost on top. Behind camera, to Robinson's End. 26th April 1986. (A. J. Cocklin)

supplying power to the quarry machines. The course of the line to Pilton crossroads is still as left after the removal of track, of which some sleepers of wood and half sleepers of concrete remain, and happily the unique double bridge is intact. The tramway route to Wing pit can be followed as far as the occupation crossing, but beyond that has been ploughed up; Wing pit itself is now a well-grown plantation near the road but with the area nearer Wing village turned over to grassland. Up to 1976 the final gullet of Scott's pit and the course of the line to it, carpeted with a limestone flora, were intact and with a two-foot gauge side-tipper body still present. The northern pit has been restored, and one section planted with pines (not

Pilton Quarries. Looking east along the cutting from the double tunnels, with sleepers in situ. 28th March 1981.
(Eric Tonks)

47

apparently on hill-and-dale however, as far as can be seen). The terminal gullet of the southern pit has been acquired by Leicestershire County Council as 'Pilton Waste Disposal Site' — something of a euphemism, as a great deal of the light waste of destructible paper and non-destructible plastic gets blown over the surrounding fields and caught on hedges. The tramway route was still mainly clear in 1979 but will doubtless be filled in due course. The road from Pilton to Morcott has Scott's pit on the west side while to the east the restored land of Ancaster pit is marked by sunken fields and single hedges — with here and there a few formally planted trees, up to the point where the ground falls away below the 300-foot contour. There is also a short gullet half way along. The final face of Ancaster pit was intact in 1982, and it was even possible to see where the shovel would bite next, but this too has been acquired by Leicestershire County Council for rubbish disposal.

Footnote
1. A published report of Ransomes & Rapier electric machines here is erroneous.

Grid References

918032	BR junction
922029	Weighhouse (second one)
923028	Locomotive shed
923027	Bridge under Pilton road
926027	Robinson's End
923026	Tipping dock
911032(?)	Site of narrow gauge bridge over Green Lane
921026	Junction of lines to Wing and Ancaster Quarries
915028	Pilton tunnels
905028	Wing Pit entrance
903028	Wing Pit terminus
915021	Scott's Pit terminus
927017	Ancaster Pit terminus

Locomotives

Gauge; 2ft.0in. (mainly constructional work)

KEIGHLEY	0-4-0T	OC	OK	2484	1908			(a)	s/s by 1923	
PIXIE	0-4-0ST	OC	WB	2090	1919	6 x 9in.	1ft.7in.	New 4/1919		(1)

(a) ex Eastwell Quarries c 1919

(1) To Pitsford Quarries c 6/1923; ex Pitsford 1928; to Eaton (Basic) Quarries 1928
There may have been a third locomotive here, named DEFIANCE, details unknown

Gauge; 4ft. 8½in.

PILTON	0-6-0ST	OC	AE	1832	1919	15 x 20in.	3ft.6in.	New 1919	(1)
IRENE	0-6-0ST	IC	MW	1359	1896	15 x 22in.	3ft.9in.	(a)	(2)
STAMFORD	0-6-0ST	OC	AE	1972	1927	15 x 20in.	3ft.6in.	New 2/1927	(3)
STAVELEY	0-6-0ST	OC	WB	2629	1941	15 x 22in.	3ft.4½in.	New 2/1941	(4)
SIR BERKELEY	0-6-0ST	IC	MW	1210	1891	12 x 18in.	3ft.0in.	(b)	(5)
		Reb MW			1909				
CRANFORD No. 2	0-6-0ST	OC	WB	2668	1942	15 x 22in.	3ft.4½in.	(c)	(6)

(a) ex Midland Ironstone Co Ltd, Crosby, Lincolnshire, c 1922
(b) ex Cranford Quarries c 1943
(c) ex Cranford Quarries 1946

(1) to G. Cohen Sons & Co Ltd, Cransley for scrap 11/1969; Scr. 11/1969
(2) to Pitsford Quarries c 1931: returned c 1935 (?). s/s
(3) to Cranford Quarries, loan and return; to Bluebell Railway, Sussex 10/1969
(4) to Midland Ironstone Co Ltd c 1943; ex Midland Ironstone 1947; to Sheepbridge Co Ltd Desborough Quarries 12/1955; ex Desborough 10/1956; to Cohen, Cransley for scrap 11/1969
(5) to Cranford Quarries 1947
(6) to Cranford Quarries 1946

Quarry Machines

No. 20	S.Navvy Crane. Rail	RH	569	1918	2¼ Cu.Yds.	26ft.	New 3/1918	(1)
No. 5	S.Navvy	RH	571	1919	⅝ Cu.Yd.		New 10/1919	(2)
No. 30	S.Shovel. Rail	RH	640	1920	2 Cu.Yds.	75ft.	New 12/1920	(3)
No. 20	S.Shovel. Caterpillar	RH	780	1923	2¾ Cu.Yds.	31ft.	New 8/1923	(4)
No. 5A	S.Transporter	RH	834	1924			New 9/1924	(5)
No. 20	S.Navvy. Long jib. Rail	RH	623	1920	1½ Cu.Yds.	58ft.	(a)	(6)
No. 15	S.Shovel. Rail	RH	704	1922	2¼ Cu.Yds.	28ft.	(b)	(7)
No. 20	S.Shovel. Rail	RH	1059	1926	2½ Cu.Yds.	24ft.	(c)	(8)
	S.Transporter	S&P	4283	1940			New 1940	(9)
43RB	D.Dragline	RB	5143	1940	1 Cu.Yd.	60ft.	New 1/1940	(10)
43RB	D.Shovel	RB	5144	1940	1¾ Cu.Yds.	22ft.	New 1/1940	(11)
43RB	D.Digger	RB	5608	1940			(d)	(12)
5W	DE.Walking Dragline	RB	14240	1951	4 Cu.Yds.	135ft.	New 10/1951	(13)
54RB	E.Shovel	RB	18342	1954			New 9/1954	(14)
5W	E.Walking Dragline	RB	19344	1955	4 Cu.Yds.	135ft.	New 8/1955	(15)
43RB	D.Dragline	RB	4876	1940	1 Cu.Yd.	70ft.	(e)	(16)

(a) ex Lamport Quarries, c 1929
(b) ex Cranford Quarries, 1931
(c) ex Logan & Hemingway, contractors, 1938
(d) ex Staveley Ironworks, c1953
(e) ex Loddington Quarries, 9/1963

(1) New to Ancaster pit, loading. Scr 1950 by Burrows of Ketton
(2) Used on constructional work with PIXIE, then probably on calcine. Scr by Thos. W. Ward Ltd
(3) New to Ancaster pit, with transporter. Scr 1960
(4) New to Scotts pit, stripping. Used with RH 834. Scr by Thos. W. Ward Ltd
(5) New to Ancaster pit; to Scotts pit, 1940. Used with RH 780. Scr 1954
(6) at Ancaster pit. To Lamport Quarries, c 1935
(7) at Scotts pit, loading. Scr 1954
(8) at Scotts pit, on calcine. Scr 1954
(9) New to Ancaster pit. Used with RH 640. Scr c 1961
(10) New to Wing pit. Possibly to Scotts pit. To Richard Thomas & Baldwins Ltd, Wansford Quarries, c 1967
(11) New to Wing pit. To Midland Ironstone Co Ltd, Crosby, Scunthorpe, 1959
(12) at Ancaster or Scotts pit. s/s
(13) New to Scotts pit. To ?, Middlesbrough, per F. G. Cann, dealer, 7/1967
(14) New to Ancaster pit. To Corby steelworks, loading coal and scr. there
(15) New to Ancaster pit. To Corby quarries (Shotley) c 1969
(16) at Ancaster pit. To Loddington Quarries c 1965

COTTESMORE QUARRIES

Owners: Sheepbridge Coal & Iron Co Ltd; Frodingham Iron & Steel Co Ltd from 14th April 1932: Appleby-Frodingham Steel Co Ltd from October 1934: United Steel Cos Ltd from 28th June 1946: U.S.C. Ore Mining Branch from 1st July 1947.

The essential features of the group of quarries centred on Cottesmore are best appreciated by approaching from the neat village of Ashwell, that in pre-Beeching days boasted a station on the Syston-Peterborough line. Alighting here and passing through the village, the walker traversed the northern end of the Vale of Catmose, threaded by the derelict but still recognisable remains of the Oakham canal, and saw before him the smooth slope of the Oolitic Cliff, here about one hundred feet high and stretching without break into the distance in each direction. The upper level is a windy plateau very rich in ironstone that outcropped at the escarpment and which was quarried extensively in an almost unbroken line for about ten miles from Burley in the south to Colsterworth in the north. The southern end was the nearest to a main line railway and was therefore developed first, but even that required the provision of a mineral

Cottesmore Quarries. Cottesmore Gorse Exchange Sidings, with 48376 picking up a load of iron ore. Note the MR lattice signal guarding the road crossing. The white building to the left of the signal is the lorry shed of the Cottesmore quarries. (M. Winnett)

line in the form of the two-mile long Cottesmore branch, starting from the Midland Railway about a third of a mile north of Ashwell station and finishing at buffer stops by the Ashwell-Cottesmore road.

In 1879 the Sheepbridge Coal & Iron Co Ltd opened discussions with Lord Gainsborough of Exton Hall and an agreement to lease ironstone was signed on 25th November 1880. It was hoped that all workable land in the parishes of Cottesmore and Barrow would be included in the lease, but it seems that only the Cottesmore parish was actually covered, as the Barrow area was leased to James Pain at a later date. The date of executing the lease was deferred until powers were obtained for the tramway to cross roads and to connect with the MR branch, and the contract for constructing the tramway was given to a Mr. Eldred. This information comes from the Sheepbridge board minutes. *Mining Journal* of 25th February 1882 states that 'A large field of ore... is about to be worked, the Midland Railway having constructed a line to it but which is not yet complete.' The branch was completed by the end of October 1882, according to Sheepbridge board minutes and was opened for goods traffic on 27th November 1882; there never was any passenger traffic, of course. Iron ore production commenced in 1882, according to MS, and before the MR branch was opened the ore was carried by horse and cart to Ashwell station. A royalty of 6d per ton was paid from 1885. It seems likely that the Cottesmore branch was opened for traffic when Sheepbridge had completed their tramway. This was of three feet gauge, ending at a tipping dock on the east side of the branch about one hundred yards short of the terminus, from which empty wagons were run as required beneath the dock and then made up into trains. From the tipping dock a quarter-mile cable-worked incline ascended the escarpment obliquely (presumably to reduce the steepness of the slope, which averaged about 1 in 13), passing beneath the road en route, and at the summit extended along level ground to the working face. The ore was under shallow cover — about six feet at the turn of the century — that was removed by hand, and the tramway equipment was of the simplest. For a line opened as late as 1882 it is strange that animal traction should have been decided upon, and in fact the Cottesmore system was the last one of any size to be worked by horses from the outset, though horses continued on existing ironstone systems and were employed on some later but small tramways.

A lease from the Ecclesiastical Commissioners, executed through the Rev. C. E. Ellwood and others, of 41 acres of Cottesmore Glebe, was obtained, dated 26th November 1914. This lay north of the Ashwell road and west of the road to Market Overton, but only the area between the

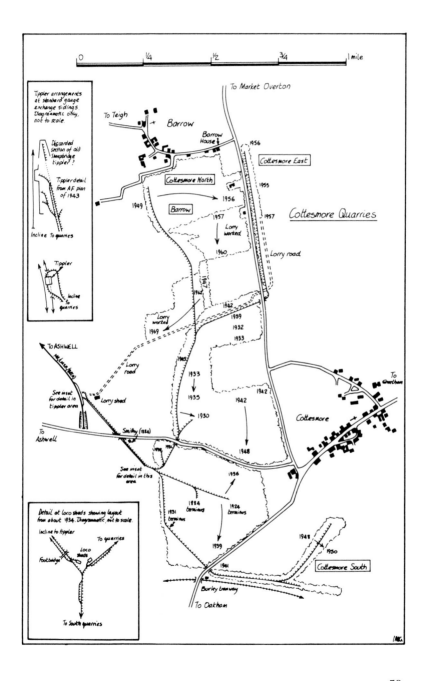

roads from Cottesmore to Ashwell and to Oakham were quarried up to 1920; GSM states that quarrying 'later may extend north' — presumably north of the Ashwell road. The OS maps for 1906 and 1915 show a single line only from the top of the incline. At the head of this was a drum fitted with a long lever brake, and loaded tubs were lowered to the tipping shed by cable, hauling up a similar number of empties at the same time. Mr. W. J. Hudson, manager of the Easton-on-the-Hill quarries, visited Cottesmore and reported his findings to Lord Exeter; in his report of 20th May 1903, he states that the incline equipment was of 'very simple construction' and quotes the wagon dimensions as 4ft. 6in. by 3ft. 3in., holding 26 cwt (33 cubic feet) of ore. Precise details of the tipping device are lacking, but traces of a retaining wall alongside the standard gauge tracks suggested that side-tippers were used. A few wagons of this type were on site in 1954, with dimensions 4ft. 0in. long by 4ft. 10in. wide and 2ft. 4in. deep; these dimensions differ from Hudson's so possibly there was more than one type, and it seems difficult to explain their presence other than for use on the old incline. A likely explanation is that these larger wagons were introduced during World War I or just after, when heavier track, a steam locomotive and a steam digger were acquired.

Cottesmore Quarries. 300 (KS3085) outside the shed. This was the only locomotive here while Sheepbridge were operating the site, but it was not used a great deal. 1st September 1947. (G. Alliez. Courtesy B. D. Stoyel)

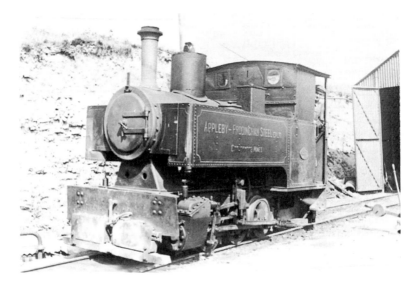

It appears however that Sheepbridge had plans for improving the transport facilities before the war; on 29th October 1912 they wrote to Pecketts, the locomotive builders of Bristol, asking for a three-foot gauge locomotive capable of hauling 25 tons up a gradient of 1/80; followed on 1st May 1913 by a letter asking for a petrol-driven locomotive to do the same work[1]. Peckett's replies are not available and the proposals — which evidently involved replacing the incline by a more lengthy line with a gentle slope, perhaps a zigzag — were put aside. Nevertheless, as stated, some mechanisation was introduced; a ten-ton navvy was purchased in 1916 and used for stripping and resoiling. At this time GSM records two pits — No. 1 with the face working northwards, and No. 2 with the face working west, towards the outcrop; the latter was presumably operated by a branch or extension tramway running south from the eastern end of the main tramway.

The steam locomotive did not come until November 1922, and was a Kerr Stuart side tank, somewhat ungainly in appearance and not very large. She was the only locomotive used during the Sheepbridge company's tenure, when almost the whole of the production went to the company's own furnaces for making forge iron, but with some being sent to Renishaw and Irlam ironworks. It was stated by the staff however that the steam locomotive was only used intermittently, horses still being regularly employed. According to company records in BSC archives, the quarries were closed from June to December 1926 in the aftermath of the General Strike. By this time much of the ground south of the Ashwell road had been exhausted, and about 1925 a tramway branch was taken under the road to open up the Glebe area on the north side, where the face was about a quarter mile long. Mr. S. H. (later Professor) Beaver visited Cottesmore in April 1930 and he describes it as a very old-fashioned system, with hand working at the face and horse haulage on the tramway, contrasting strongly with its mechanised neighbours at Burley and Market Overton.[2] The locomotive was presumably in its shed, unused, and the fate of the steam digger is unknown. Professor Beaver goes on to describe the methods used; the cover was removed by hand and transferred to the worked-out area; the ore was hewn out by pick, and the top was then prised down by crowbars, some ten men being employed to heave down a section 3-4 yards long. Each loader filled 15 or 16 wagons per day.

But the end was in sight for Sheepbridge here; in 1928 they were approached by Dorman Long & Co Ltd with the aim of subletting 89 acres of the Cottesmore lease, evidently for incorporating in their Burley operation, but nothing seems to have come of this and in October 1929 negotiations began with the Frodingham Iron & Steel Co Ltd, at first for operating the Cottesmore quarries jointly, and then for Frodingham to take over completely, but with a clause entitling Sheepbridge to Cottesmore ore should they ask for it. Sheepbridge ceased operations at the end of March 1932 and the Gainsborough lease was surrendered on 30th March 1933, Frodingham taking over with a new lease on the 31st; the existing Ecclesiastical Commissioners' lease in respect of Cottesmore Glebe was assigned to Frodingham. Frodingham commenced by extending the final Sheepbridge gullet as far as the Market Overton road, then working southward, which was continued up to 1941.

As already stated, the Sheepbridge leases covered a wide area and adjoined the south end of Pain's Market Overton lease, but only a comparatively small area had been developed, and the pits were shallow enough to be outside the jurisdiction of H. M. Inspector of Quarries. Frodingham planned to develop the area fully by mechanising the quarry operations, for which they purchased in 1933 a pair of diesel machines — a 43RB dragline and a 37RB shovel — and by re-equipping the tramway. The most important change was the remodelling of the transfer arrangements at the Cottesmore branch terminus; in June 1934 fabrication began of a rotary tippler, that was brought into use on 20th March 1935, and at the same time the incline machinery was improved. Cable operation was continued, with a drum at the incline head under the control of a

Cottesmore Quarries. View down incline from above the bridge under the Ashwell road, 24th October 1948. Note runaway siding at right. (Eric Tonks)

Cottesmore Quarries. View up incline towards bridge under the Ashwell road. Empty tubs ascending on left, full tubs descending on right. 24th October 1948.   (Eric Tonks)

Cottesmore Quarries. Empty 3ft. gauge tubs at foot of incline, waiting to be hauled up by cable, 24th October 1948. Road for full wagons to left. (Eric Tonks)

brakesman. Steel tubs, 4ft. 10in. long, 3ft. 8in. wide and 2ft. 3in. deep, with roller bearings to the wheels, and holding approximately 35 cwt of ore were used (*The Northampton Sand Ironstone in South Lincolnshire and Rutland*, by R. J. M. Dixie, September 1973 (in BSC archives) quotes two tons). These tubs were clipped singly or in pairs to the cable; at the foot of

Cottesmore Quarries. Tipping stage over the BR siding 24th October 1948. Hopper wagon being loaded. (Eric Tonks)

Cottesmore Quarries.
Lunch break at the top of
the incline. Note the score
marks on the wagon sides,
made by the 'gripper bars'
used to prevent runaways.
c 1940.   (RRM Archives/
L. Boddington Collection)

the incline the shackle was released and the tub was pushed by hand to the
short slope leading to the tippler; under the rails on this slope ran a
continuous steel belt with projecting teeth that engaged the axles and
propelled the tub to the tippler, into which it was pushed manually,
reversed and emptied into a railway wagon beneath, and pushed to the
exit side by the next wagon, thence running down by gravity to the foot of
the incline, where it was reclipped to the cable. The wagons were loose-
coupled and unbraked but chance runaways from the top of the incline
could be arrested by a braking device in the control of the cable operator;
this consisted of two wooden bars, one on each side of and about 2ft. 6in.
above rail level, and by pulling a lever the brakesman could make the bars
grip the sides of a tub passing between them. The steepest part of the
incline was the section between the summit and the bridge under the road,
and successful working depended on the impetus gained during the initial
descent; this made the incline rather more difficult to operate than some
others. By the winding drum there was a footbridge over the line, which
was in cutting at this point. On the standard gauge, Appleby-Frodingham
used 20-ton wagons, of which they possessed 500 (R. J. M. Dixie, quoted
above).

The motive power was also mechanised, and it is doubtful if
Frodingham used horses at all; probably they used the Kerr Stuart for any
production in 1933. By this time the value of diesel locomotive for narrow
gauge tramways was becoming firmly established, and two machines
were obtained from Ruston & Hornsby Ltd; the first, in 1934, was of class
22/28HP and was found to be somewhat underpowered for the work it was
expected to do, and a more powerful 36/42HP machine—the first of its

Cottesmore Quarries. 310 (RH 168843) bringing a train from the quarries past the loco. shed. This train will then be propelled towards the incline top. 1934.

(Ruston & Hornsby)

class—arrived a year later. Ruston & Hornsby records suggest that a third locomotive may have been here; 177536, also of 36/42HP class, was supplied to Appleby Frodingham works at Scunthorpe, but between October 1939 and February 1942 spares were supplied to 'Colsterworth Mines', to which all spares for the other two locomotives were consigned. This information only came to light in 1984, from the RH spares files, rather late to get confirmation from local sources, so it is only quoted as a possibility.

The diesels on the whole did not prove fully satisfactory, and steam once again became the order of the day with the acquisition of two secondhand locomotives, including a Kerr Stuart of the same type as the earlier one. The first four engines were numbered 30-33 in order of acquisition, i.e. following the Frodingham Works series 1-29, but from 1938 a cipher was added to the numbers to prevent confusion with new standard gauge locomotives at Frodingham numbered in the 30s. The next two engines became 340 and 350. The livery of these engines was green, lined red and yellow, except that 320 retained its original green lined black edged with white. The owners' name (Appleby-Frodingham Steel Co Ltd, later changed to United Steel Cos Ltd) and *COTTESMORE MINES* were painted on the tanks in yellow with red shading. The Hudswell Clarke 0-4-0ST carried its Derby Riverlands numberplate for some time, upside down, but was usually

Cottesmore Quarries. The second Kerr Stuart on the site, No. 340 (KS 3089) outside the new locomotive shed. Note footbridge over cutting. 1st July 1952.

(K. Cooper/IRS Collection)

Cottesmore Quarries. 30 (HC 1225) outside the old loco. shed. 22nd October 1948.

(C. P. Knight)

Cottesmore Quarries. 350 (HC 1736) at work 1st September 1947, with a train from the quarries. This neat little locomotive was rather under-powered for the work and thus not very popular.

(G. Alliez. Courtesy B. D. Stoyel)

Cottesmore Quarries. The locomotive sheds. Original shed on right, with the line to the quarries beyond the locomotive. Newer shed to left, in front of water tower. 23rd September 1954.   (G. Alliez. Courtesy B. D. Stoyel)

referred to as *GRANGE*, its former name. A further engine was added to stock in 1943; this unusual machine was an exceedingly neat little six-coupled pannier tank, painted plain green, with short wheelbase, outside Walschaert's valve gear and coal bunkers by the cabsides; unfortunately, the boiler was too small and the engine was never popular, and in less than ten years the firebox was worn out.

The original locomotive shed was of corrugated iron with a louvre in the roof, and was capable of holding the Kerr Stuarts only. In 1934 an extension in the same constructional material was made at the rear end to accommodate the diesel. At a later date a separate shed was built on the other side of the footbridge. The layout in the shed area was modified about the same time.

The Frodingham company rapidly developed the area north of the Cottesmore-Ashwell road, extending the tramway as far as the parish boundary south of Barrow, which was the limit of the lease. A pair of machines similar to the existing pair, i.e. a 43RB dragline and a 37RB shovel, were purchased in 1939 to speed up production, and by 1941 the southern part of the area had been exhausted and lay partly waterlogged. In that year Cottesmore South pit was opened, southeast of the Cottesmore-Oakham road, the tramway to serve this passing beneath this road by a tunnel adjacent to that of the Burley quarry tramway. The stone

Cottesmore Quarries. Quarry view, 28th May 1945. 43RB diesel dragline for removing the shallow overburden; and also can be seen the jib of the 37RB diesel shovel for loading the ironstone. Note the corn growing on the worked-out ground to the right. (BGS)

Cottesmore Quarries. Cottesmore South quarry in May 1949, with the 5W walking dragline removing overburden. This quarry, much deeper that the others serviced by the narrow gauge tramway, and requiring more massive machines, was later connected by branch to the standard gauge Exton park system. (BGS)

here was initially outcrop but the cover increased to 20 feet and from about 1947 it was removed by a 5W Ruston Bucyrus walking dragline. A new pit, Cottesmore North, working clockwise between the escarpment east of Barrow village and the Cottesmore-Market Overton road, was opened in 1948, bringing traffic to the northern branch of the tramway that had been disused for several years. This area, in Barrow parish, had originally been leased to James Pain as part of his Market Overton system, and was purchased by Appleby-Frodingham; Pain's successors, Stanton Ironworks Co Ltd, worked their Barrow pit north of the lane to the village. Cottesmore North pit was operated by a Ruston Bucyrus 3W dragline and a 43RB shovel, working clockwise from the escarpment towards the Market Overton road. A small strip of land immediately north of the Ashwell road was also worked 1946-48. At this time, operations at Cottesmore South were coming to an end as plans were made for the big development at Exton Park, which included a branch to work Cottesmore South, where the stone was under increasing cover. The finish of narrow gauge working at Cottesmore South is not recorded but was probably 1950, as the survey plans show the annual strips quarried to be wider from then onwards. The

Cottesmore Quarries. The two Hudswell Clarkes, greatly differing in design, out of use in 1955 on a siding alongside the line to Cottesmore South quarry.   (Collection Eric Tonks)

Cottesmore Quarries. As the Kerr Stuart and Hudswell Clarke locomotives were not up to the heavier work demanded by the longer line to Cottesmore North quarry, United Steels purchased four locomotives of Peckett design from John Lysaght's Scunthorpe Works. They were done up in Colsterworth shops and three were put into service at Cottesmore in 1952. 301 was actually built by Lysaght's from parts supplied by Peckett. Photograph c 1954.   (F. Jones)

new Exton Park line partly followed the course of the former narrow gauge metals, which were then lifted from a point just short of the Oakham road to make way, and the narrow gauge south of the locomotive sheds was thenceforward disused except for storing excess stock. The latter included the two Hudswell Clarkes, both of which were in need of extensive overhaul.

The Kerr Stuarts were not in good enough condition to work the route to Cottesmore North pit; but it so happened that John Lysaghts Ltd had planned to replace the three-foot system at Normanby Park Works by standard gauge, and the four locomotives (two built by Pecketts and two built by Lysaghts from parts supplied by Pecketts) were going cheap—cheaper in fact than a new firebox for the pannier! In June 1952 three of them were sent to Cottesmore and No. 2 retained as a spare at Colsterworth shops; they were repainted in the standard livery of green with red and yellow lining and renumbered by adding 300 to those carried at Scunthorpe, thus obscuring the origin of the 3XO numbers of the earlier locomotives. The new arrivals were fitted with low buffers and centre couplings suited to the tubs and immediately assumed complete control of the traffic from the pits, handling trains of 30-36 loaded tubs. The trains

Cottesmore Quarries. Sister locomotive 303 at Cottesmore yard 23rd September 1954. This locomotive had slightly smaller wheels than its sisters, and was the only one that could clear the footbridge near the incline top. (G. Alliez. Courtesy B. D. Stoyel)

Cottesmore Quarries. 304 at the shed. Note how large this engine is compared with the Ruston & Hornsby diesel. (F. Jones)

arriving from the pits were placed in the loop by the locomotive shed junction. The section between here and the top of the incline was normally worked by one of the diesels or, if they were both laid up, by a Kerr stuart; the low bridge on this section would not permit two of the Pecketts through though, oddly enough, one of them (No. 303) had just that inch or so difference to enable it to be used in an emergency; she had smaller diameter wheels than the others. These engines also differed in other minor ways, e.g. the shape of the sheet flanking the smokebox front, and in the possession or otherwise of sliding window shutters. The quarry traffic required the use of two 'Pecketts' daily to work the 1½ miles to Barrow; the track incidentally was flat-bottomed, spiked to wooden sleepers and on curves was held in position by timbers ramped against the edge of the trackbed.

In March 1954 plans were in hand to open a fresh pit (Cottesmore East) east of the Cottesmore-Market Overton road, to be reached by tunneling beneath the latter; hitherto quarrying had extended to, but not beyond, this road. The first gullet was driven in 1955. It seemed probable, therefore, that there was still a considerable expectation of life to this system, which had much of interest historically, in operating methods and locomotive stock. The last-named probably attracted the enthusiast most and

Cottesmore Quarries. Loading dock with a loaded Aveling-Barford lorry awaiting the arrival of railway wagons. Another lorry stands empty. Note the 'butterfly' arrangement to deflect stone into the wagons. c 1960.   (RRM Archives; original by BSC)

certainly showed variety, comprising the pair of oddly-assorted Hudswell Clarkes relegated to the rail-end by the Oakham road, the two Kerr Stuarts squashed in the diesel shed after languishing for some time in the open at Cottesmore North, and the three 'Pecketts', which were kept in beautiful condition. One cold snowy day early in 1956 the Hudswell Clarkes were removed for scrap and a few yards of track at the end taken up, 340 being moved to the new terminus. The proposed new line referred to above was built in 1954, passing beneath the road by Warren Farm and then running parallel to the road as far as the Barrow turn. Unfortunately however conditions were less happy than they appeared; the Pecketts, whilst superior to their predecessors in hauling power by virtue of their 12-inch cylinders, were heavy on the track, even though it had been relaid from the original light 35 lb rail to a much heavier rail obtained secondhand from Bicester, and it was decided to dispense with the narrow gauge and replace it either by a standard gauge branch from the Exton Park system or by lorry haulage; and after some experiments the latter alternative was selected. The tramway was operated for the last time on 8th June 1957, and dismantling by USC men commenced in August with the removal of track and equipment connected with the incline; scrapping of the 200 or so wagons followed and finally the remaining locomotive stock — except for the larger diesel, which was transferred to Dragonby Mines. The locomotives were cut up in the period October to December 1957, the last steamers being 301, followed by 310.

While these melancholy events were taking place, construction of the new transport system was going ahead; a concrete tipping dock, with 'butterfly' guard to prevent spillage on the track, was constructed on the site of the tippler, and from it a 25-feet wide concrete lorry road was laid, ascending the bank obliquely in the opposite direction to the tramway incline and then running directly towards the Cottesmore-Market Overton road, practically on the route of the final gullet in this direction. It did not pass under the road however but in side-stepping fashion climbed to road level and crossed to the workings on the east side of the road. A branch road of crushed limestone led from the main section of concrete road to the

Cottesmore Quarries. Loading dock for lorries at Cottesmore Sidings. The quarries had been closed, but the sidings remained intact, and further along were used to serve Exton Park Quarries. 7th July 1972.   (J. R. Bonser)

Cottesmore Quarries. The lorry road, looking towards Cottesmore Sidings. By the oak tree the road turns left down a sharp incline to the tipping dock area. 5th September 1977.

(Eric Tonks)

Barrow pits. Apart from the replacement of the picturesque tramway by three Euclid dumpers of 1958, the quarries continued as before, the ore travelling down the Cottesmore branch. The lorry road to the quarry ran parallel to and west of the public road and working continued southwards to about the end of 1960, when another area was opened up nearer the escarpment, and reached by another branch lorry road on the site of the first

Cottesmore Quarries. Parapet of the bridge where the narrow gauge line ran beneath to reach Cottesmore East quarry, looking from the west towards the Market Overton road. December 1980. The building to the right is a substation for supplying power for the quarry machines. (Eric Tonks)

rail route to Barrow pits. In July 1961 the quarries were closed temporarily but were reopened and worked in a small way until the middle of 1964, the exact date of closure not being recorded.

Traces of the tramway steadily diminished. By 1964 the locomotive sheds had gone, but the water tank was left in position and still is. The bridges under the Ashwell-Cottesmore road had also been filled in; the bridge under the Cottesmore-Market Overton road was left intact, and the parapets, solidly made of cast concrete blocks, remain, though the bridge is filled in beneath. The quarried area west of this road was levelled and the more recent and obvious quarries were part filled with refuse, brought by lorry, for which the concrete road proved very useful. This was done in the early 1960s and the ground was returned to cultivation. East of the Cottesmore-Market Overton road lay the long narrow gullet — it never became more than that before quarrying ceased in 1957, as the ore was not up to expectations; this was becoming prettily overgrown with goat willow, a typical tree in this situation, when the refuse lorries started to move in about 1964, but it was not until 1976 that the job was completed and the tip closed. Corn was soon growing on this restored strip — but not for long, as in 1979 the area was stony, given over to nettles, thistles and other rough herbage. The last quarry machines, the 3W and 43RB, stood on the concrete road near the top of the incline, where they had been dumped since the closure, and disappeared about 1972.

The concrete road is the most permanent exhibit; it is used by the farming people and even by driving schools teaching learners in the early stages! The older quarrying areas towards Cottesmore are crossed by replacement hedges of pure hawthorn, those towards Barrow by wire fences or by hawthorn and elder. The ground is mostly arable, with a plantation (mostly on a 'washout' devoid of ironstone) near the parish boundary with Barrow. Of the tramway it is hard to find any traces at all; the incline route south of the Ashwell road can just be picked out by slight depressions in the ground and the presence of coarse weeds, and with the water tower to give an initial 'fix'. North of the road is a smaller triangular spinney wherein are some interesting remains in the form of the tramway cutting and, among the trees, a much bent and battered steel tub body and some lengths of steel cable. It is said that tubs lie buried in the blocked-up tunnel beneath the road.

The BR sidings, heavily overgrown, remained until the Cottesmore branch was lifted in 1974, and the site became later the headquarters of the Market Overton Industrial Railway Association when this body had to vacate their Market Overton premises. Preliminary work on the site commenced in the summer of 1979 and the bulk of the locomotives and rolling stock moved across in December. By dint of sustained effort and sheer hard work the Association has built up its collection and has become increasingly oriented towards the ironstone industry, with the construction of a museum devoted to the industry as its ultimate aim. In 1981 the Association changed its name to the Rutland Railway Museum, in keeping with this objective and happily retaining a further link with the past in the name of the smallest county. Much clearance of the site has been necessary, and at the side of the premises can be seen the concrete tipping dock used by lorries, and to the right may be seen traces of the earlier tippler wall.

The north end of Cottesmore South pit has sunk sufficiently to become permanently flooded, colonised by water plants and the home of coot; nearby the stables used by Sheepbridge more than half a century ago still stand.

Footnotes

1. Peckett records, extracted by Mr. K. P. Plant
2. Rutland Record No. 3: 1982/3 p.110

Cottesmore Quarries. Horses were used on the Cottesmore system throughout the time Sheepbridge were operating, 1883 to 1932. In the centre of the picture can be seen the stables where the horses were kept, in Cottesmore village. 13th November 1985.

(Eric Tonks)

Grid References

887135	BR sidings terminus
887138	Original tipping dock
890134	Top of incline
891134	Locomotive sheds
891135	Water tank
889135	Bridge under Ashwell road (incline)
892135	Bridge under Ashwell road (quarry)
894127	Bridge under Oakham road
897143	Bridge under Market Overton road
890150 approx.	Barrow Pit terminus
896152	Roadside pit terminus
887137	Concrete road — tipping dock
889141	Concrete road — top of incline
897144	Concrete road — road crossing
893142	Concrete road — branch terminus

Locomotives

Gauge; 3ft. 0in.

300	(30 until c1938)	0-6-0T	OC	KS	3085	1917	8½ x 11in.	1ft.11⅝in.	(a)	Scr 1/1957
310	(31 until c1938)	4wDM		RH	168843	1934	22/28HP cls	4ton		New 2/1934
										Scr 12/1957
320	(32 until c1938)	4wDM		RH	174204	1935	36/42HP cls	5½ton		New 1/1935 (1)
330	(33 until c1938)	0-4-0ST	OC	HC	1225	1916	6½ x 12in.	1ft.11in.	(b)	Scr 2/1956
340		0-6-0T	OC	KS	3089	1917	8½ x 11in.	1ft.11⅝in.	(c)	Scr 1/1957
350		0-6-0PT	OC	HC	1736	1943	8½ x 12in.	2ft.0in.		New 3/1943
										Scr 2/1956
No.301	(No. 1 to 1953)	0-4-0ST	OC		Lysaght	1946	12 x 18in.	3ft.0½in.	(d)	Scr 12/1957
No.303	(No.3 until 1953)	0-4-0ST	OC	P	1498	1918	12 x 18in.	2ft.9½in.	(d)	Scr 11/1957
No.304	(No.4 until 1953)	0-4-0ST	OC	P	1317	1913	12 x 18in.	3ft.0½in.	(d)	Scr c 11/1957

(a) ex Alexander Hannell, dealers, Slough c 1922; f. Ministry of Munitions, Timber Supply Depot, Nairn.

(b) ex Derby Riverlands Improvement Contract, Alvaston, per H. Potter, dealer, Nottingham 12/1935

(c) ex Thos. W. Ward Ltd, 12/1939; previously Lehane MacKenzie & Shand Ltd, contractors, Fernilee Reservoir.

(d) ex John Lysaght's Scunthorpe Works Ltd 6/1952

(1) to Dragonby Mines, Scunthorpe c 8/1957

Quarry Machines

	No. 20	S. Navvy	RP	472	1916	2¼ Cu.Yds.	26ft.	New 2/1916	s/s
	43RB	D. Dragline	RB	2378	1933	1¼ Cu.Yds.	55ft.	New 11/1933	s/s
	37RB	D. Shovel	RB	2379	1933	1½ Cu.Yds.	40ft.	New 11/1933	s/s
	43RB	D. Dragline	RB	4044	1939	½ Cu.Yd.	60ft.	New 2/1939	(1)
	37RB	D. Shovel	RB	4045	1939	1½ Cu.Yds.	40ft.	New 2/1939	(2)
	5W	E. Walking Dragline	RB	9215	1946	4 Cu.Yds.	135ft.	New 8/1946	(3)
1040	3W	D. Walking Dragline	RB	14572	1952	2½ Cu.Yds.	90ft.	New 3/1952	(4)
1091	43RB	D. Shovel	RB	18353	1954	1½ Cu.Yds.	60ft.	(a)	(4)

(a) ex Burley Quarries

(1) to Colsterworth Quarries c 1960
(2) to Burley Quarries c 1963
(3) At Cottesmore South quarry. To Exton Park Quarries when the latter took over the quarry, c 1950.
(4) At Cottesmore North quarry. s/s c 1972.

BURLEY QUARRIES

Owners: Bell Bros Ltd; Dorman Long & Co Ltd from April 1923; Dorman Long (Steel) Ltd from 3rd October 1954; United Steel Cos Ltd, Ore Mining Branch from 1st September 1957.

The iron and steel-making industry of Tees-side was founded on the discovery of the rich Cleveland iron ore field in the middle of the 19th century, and there was no need to supplement its supplies from elsewhere until this local source showed signs of running out, which was not until well into the 20th century. The first company to do so was Bell Bros Ltd, owners of an ironworks at Port Clarence and various collieries. Their first entry into the Midlands ironstone quarry scene, at Wakerley, very soon came to an end; but their second venture, at Burley, was much more successful, especially after the great steel-making concern of Dorman Long took them over, along with Bell Bros' business in general. On the face of things, it is surprising that Bell Bros — 200 miles away — should discover the existence of iron ore at Burley, but the 1899 board minutes of Staveley Coal & Iron Co Ltd record that they had considered leasing 450 acres of the Burley estate but had not taken it up, one of the main difficulties being the necessity to build cottages for workers; possibly Bell Bros learnt of this. The lease with the Hanbury estate of Burley consisted of about 500 acres east of the Cottesmore-Oakham road, from a point south of where their tramway was taken under the road (i.e. south of Sheepbridge's Cottesmore lease) to the corner of the by-road to Burley Bushes; the boundary then followed this road as far as the stream and along the west bank of the latter much of the distance to the northern boundary that was almost due east from the main road. There was also a strip on the west side of the main road for a similar distance from south to north, totalling about 100 acres.

In November 1919 a labour force of twelve men started work on the construction of the tramway system, which was in two sections; a standard gauge line that ran from a junction with the Midland Railway Cottesmore branch—officially titled Cottesmore Gorse Exchange Sidings—about a quarter of a mile from the terminus in a southerly direction along the foot of the Oolitic Cliff for a mile; and a three-foot gauge tramway from the workings to a tipping stage alongside the standard gauge, with a cable-worked incline down the Cliff. The system therefore followed the example of their neighbours at Cottesmore very closely in spite of the latter's being then nearly 40 years old, and the Burley narrow gauge incline was in fact

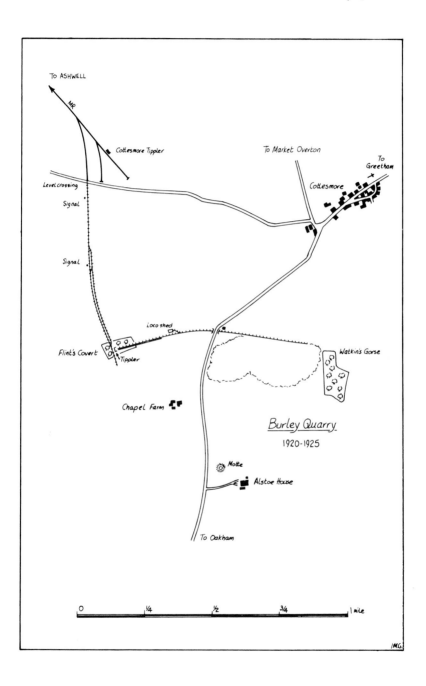

To ASHWELL

MR

Cottesmore Tippler

To Market Overton

To Greetham

Cottesmore

Level crossing

Signal

Signal

Loco shed

Watkin's Gorse

Flint's Covert

Tippler

Chapel Farm

Burley Quarry

1920-1925

Motte

Alstoe House

To Oakham

0   ¼   ½   ¾   1 mile

IMG.

the last to be built by an ironstone company in this country. Production commenced in 1920 and a single standard gauge locomotive was transferred from Port Clarence in that year to work the lower line, replacing an earlier engine, *NORMANBY*, used during the construction: No. 24, as she was then, used to stand in the open when not in use, possibly deriving some shelter from Flint's Covert surrounding the terminus. The narrow gauge was better equipped, there being at one time three engines that were housed in a single-road shed at the summit of the incline, from which point the line entered a cutting for the rest of the run to the quarries, passing beneath the Cottesmore-Oakham road by a concrete bridge; alongside the latter were the offices, workshops and a 'sausage' water tank at road level. The locomotives comprised a Manning Wardle 0-4-0 saddle tank and a Kerr Stuart 0-4-2 side tank, both new; the wagons were V-shaped side-tippers. Operating details of the incline are not known. The ironstone was under very shallow cover (4-5 feet) and in 1942 NSI quotes six feet of ironstone with four feet overburden.

A small area adjacent to the Oakham road, south of the tramway, was worked at a date unknown but probably from the commencement; but the main workings were to the northeast of Cow Close Farm, the face running southeast from Watkin's Gorse, working westwards. Two small machines were purchased new from Ruston & Hornsby.

Bell Bros' operations here were almost as short-lived as at Wakerley but in this case it was not closure but the takeover of the company by Dorman, Long & Co Ltd in 1923. There was no immediate change in the pattern of operations and indeed early in 1925 a third locomotive was brought in on the narrow gauge; she came from Port Clarence, then in the hands of Dorman Long. The latter however evidently regarded the narrow gauge as old-fashioned and decided to use standard gauge throughout. The low-level line was extended a quarter mile and the incline replaced by a sweeping curve at about 1 in 35 up the escarpment, the route at the upper level being on the course of the former narrow gauge line. It was however found that the tunnel under the Oakham road gave insufficient clearance, and a new girder bridge was built alongside; the old bridge, fitted with doors at each end, was converted into a repair shop for wagons. It might be mentioned that two of the locomotives used on the line in later years had cut-down mountings and could have negotiated the original tunnel! Of the narrow gauge locomotives, two were sold but the Kerr Stuart was converted to standard gauge for continued use at Burley. Another curiosity was that the parapets of the narrow gauge bridge were slightly skew to the road, but those of the standard gauge were parallel. A report in BSC archives

Burley Quarries. Bridge under the Oakham road. The narrow gauge line ran to the right of this, and the tunnel it used was fitted with doors and used as a wagon repair shop. 24th October 1948. (Eric Tonks)

under the title *The Northampton Sands Ironstone in South Lincolnshire and Rutland 1870-1973* by R. J. M. Dixie; September 1973, states that the conversion to standard gauge was carried out during the General Strike of 1926.

The new standard gauge construction at the lower end consisted of bullhead rail, 95lbs per yard, on chairs cast by Dorman Long in 1925, the

Burley quarries. Most of the Burley engines tended to be covered with calcine dust from the clamps near the loco. shed. *BERYL*, however, usually took the trains from the clamps to Cottesmore exchange sidings, and was kept in nice condition, as here on 4th April 1960. Note the chairs of Dorman Long design. (S. A. Leleux)

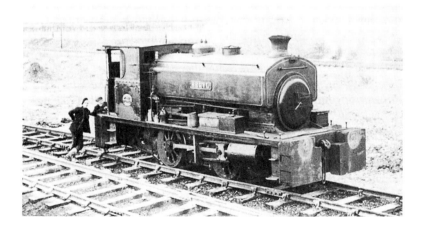

sleepers being of wood; east of the Oakham road the rails were carried on low flat chairs spiked to wooden sleepers or bolted to concrete sleepers. These chairs, with the rail clipped on, were unique as far as ironstone quarries are concerned. The approach to the level crossing with the Ashwell road was protected on each side by MR signals controlled from a ground frame. The headquarters of the system was moved from the Oakham road bridge to a point immediately southeast of Watkin's Gorse, a small piece of woodland through which the new line cut a sizeable swathe. In the centre of the area, from which the ironstone had already been removed, was a very imposing two-road locomotive shed of red brick, with four steel-framed windows on each side, a wooden louvre in the roof, and at the front and rear large double wooden doors, and a circular ventilator in the brickwork above. This shed held four locomotives and later was extended rearwards to the same pattern, increasing the number of side windows to six; the doors were re-used, but the original end was apparent from the 'partition' in the roof—the brickwork with its round ventilator. As far as is known, the stock did not exceed four until World War II, but the extension was built in the later 1930s, and it was customary for the rear portion of the shed to be used for repair work; a lifting gantry stood just outside the doors. South of the shed lay calcining clamps; it seems unlikely that calcining was carried out in narrow gauge days but it was certainly a very prominent feature later at Burley, being particularly apparent when the adjacent line to Cottesmore South and Exton Park was opened up, as United Steels did not calcine.

Burley was different from any other ironstone quarry in the country; not in principle but in the way it struck the eye. Almost every quarry had some special feature that singled it out but on the other hand it usually had something in common with other systems; the Staveley quarries all had a certain family likeness and so did those of Stanton, Stewarts & Lloyds Minerals and United Steels. But not Burley; Burley was Dorman Long's only ironstone quarry and the difference was obvious as soon as one entered the premises. The locomotives were a very mixed lot, mostly throw-outs from the northeast, of various shapes (normal and cut down) and livery (with black predominating) and clearly not from any of the usual quarry owners. Most characteristic of all, though, was the calcine dust that lay over everything; calcining darkens the colour of the ore, usually to a deep red-brown; but Burley evidently used a slightly different technique—probably a higher temperature—and the calcine was a deep purple colour.

The standard gauge system was opened for traffic in 1926, with a long

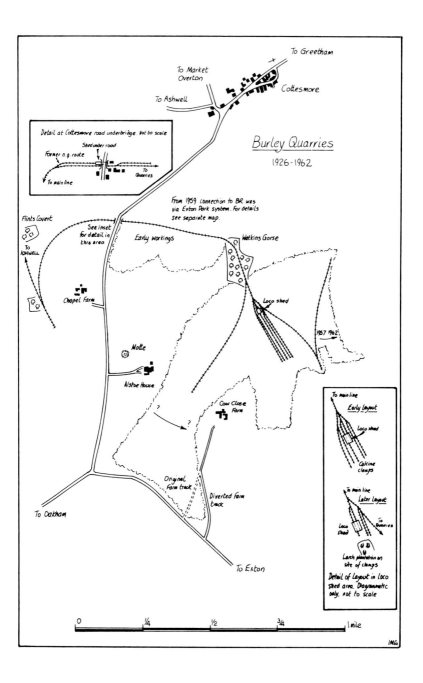

Burley Quarries
1926-1962

To Greetham

To Market
Overton

To Ashwell

Cottesmore

Detail at Cottesmore road underbridge. Not to scale

Shed under road

Former n.g. route

To main line

To Quarries

From 1959 connection to BR was
via Exton Park system. For details
see separate map.

Flints Covert

To Ashwell

See inset
for detail in
this area

Early workings

Watkins Gorse

Loco shed

1957 1962

Chapel Farm

Motte

Alstoe House

Cow Close
Farm

?

?

To main line

Early layout

Loco shed

Calcine
clamps

To main line

Later layout

Loco
shed

To
Quarries

Larch plantation on
site of clamps

Detail of Layout in Loco
shed area. Diagrammatic
only, not to scale

To Oakham

Original
farm track

Diverted farm
track

To Exton

0   ¼   ½   ¾   1 mile

JMG

81

Burley Quarries. *PATRICK* brings in a rake of 'Ship Canal' wagons that will be unloaded at the calcine clamps. c 1935.   (RRM Archives/R. Bland Collection)

face of about half a mile from the locomotive shed area to the Burley Bushes road, the face moving westwards, west of Cow Close farm and skirting Alstoe House (that still remains its 'motte'). Mr. Ayres, the occupier of Cow Close farm, gave the interesting information that the drive to the farm was diverted to the east to permit quarrying of the original route, and to this day the drive retains the awkward oblique approach to the road; the existence of trees in the hedge indicates that quarrying was not taken right

Burley Quarries. Old 'Ship canal' wagons formerly used on the calcine banks; standing outside the loco. shed. Note the recent extension to the shed, at the right. 24th October 1948.   (Eric Tonks)

up to the new alignment. Mr. Ayres also said that quarrying was suspended for several years, probably in the early 1930s.

In *Rutland Record* No. 3, 1982/3, p.113, Professor S. H. Beaver describes the working of the quarries in April 1930; the shallow overburden was removed by hand and the ore was loaded by steam shovel into wagons for conveyance to the calcine clamps, of which there were three, each holding about 40,000 tons of ore. The burnt ore was loaded by steam shovel into wagons and taken to a screening plant, worked by a vertical boiler from an old navvy; the dust was collected in wagons beneath the screens and the ore was shot into 20-ton Dorman Long hoppers. The dust was used as ballast on the rail tracks. This rather cumbrous procedure was later changed by the omission of screening and modification of the wagons. In the post-World War II years a number of wooden side-tipping wagons lay around at Burley and it is presumed that originally these were used for conveying raw stone from quarry to calcine clamp; but they were later replaced by a novel form of wagon consisting of three skips placed transversely on a couple of old rails laid along a flat wagon frame. These skips were loaded in the pit by the digger and were fitted with three hooks by which they could be lifted by steam crane at the calcine clamps, emptied and returned to the wagon frame. After being 'burnt' (a process taking about eight weeks) the ore was

Burley Quarries. Skip wagons replaced the side-tippers. Each skip was lifted by crane and emptied on the calcine bank. 24th October 1948.   (Eric Tonks)

Burley Quarries. A poor picture, but the only one we have of the No. 8 Ruston shovel. c 1935.   (RRM Archives/R. Bland Collection)

loaded into standard wagons of 21 and 28 ton capacity and taken down to the Cottesmore branch.

Our knowledge of quarry machines used in early days is probably incomplete; there was an 8-ton steam shovel and an SND No 4 transporter

Burley Quarries. 37RB diesel shovel in the quarry. c.1935.

(RRM Archives/R. Bland Collection)

Burley Quarries. *PATRICK* taking a loaded train from the quarry, 4th April 1960. The machine is a 5W walking dragline. 4th April 1960.   (S. A. Leleux)

from Rustons, the former probably for loading at the pit and the latter at the clamps; but there may well have been others (steam or diesel) particularly in Dorman Long days, that came secondhand. The first known diesel machine was a secondhand 37RB shovel: a 43RB diesel shovel came new in 1954, and a 5W diesel-electric walking dragline was in use in the middle 1950s for removing overburden. By then, quarrying had moved to east of the clamps area, reached by a line running east of the engine shed, with a reversing point en route.

When the through standard gauge line was opened in 1926, a new locomotive was delivered from Andrew Barclay, but with this exception all the locomotives in the Dorman Long regime were transferred from other works in the group; the earlier ones retained their original numbers for several years but eventually three sets of nameplates were sent down from Middlesborough for *ANGELA*, *BERYL* and *EUNICE*, so that all engines at Burley should carry names. When *EUNICE* was scrapped, its nameplates were transferred to a fresh arrival. Two of the locomotives — *JUPITER* and the second *EUNICE* — had cut-down boiler mountings, though this was of course unnecessary at Burley, and *EUNICE* had a normal cab fitted,

85

Burley Quarries. *BERYL* descends to the vale of Catmose with a loaded train; at the reversing point at the foot of the bank the train was pushed to Cottesmore Sidings. 24th October 1948.

(Eric Tonks)

making her rather odd-looking. The most unusual machine on the stock was an ancient relic formerly in the service of the Rhymney Railway and known familiarly to the staff as *ADAM*: it did not however do a lot of work. Barclays formed the bulk of the loco. stock and their sturdy simplicity was much appreciated and in later years jocularly compared with the gadget-laden Yorkshire Engines next door; the usual livery was black with red connecting rods, 5 having red lining also, while *JUPITER* and *BERYL* were green. In 1957 the former was repainted light green with red rods.

Details of locomotive duties for the earlier years are wanting, but from World War II onwards the usual roster consisted of one working the quarry, two the calcining clamps and another taking loads from Watkin's Gorse to the Cottesmore branch terminus. This last duty was normally the province of *BERYL* (she and the first *EUNICE* had 16in. cylinders, the others having 14in. or 15in.) The train had to reverse at the foot of the bank, from which it was pushed to the reception sidings past the former narrow gauge unloading stage, for weighing; a gentle slope northwards allowed the wagons to run by gravity into farther sidings, beyond which they were remarshalled into trains for the main line. *BERYL* then returned with the

Burley Quarries. The locomotive stock at Burley consisted mainly of engines no longer required at Dorman Long's works in the north east, and was a mixed bag. Two of them had cut down mountings, a feature not required at Burley of course. *EUNICE* (AB 857) shown here out of use 7th May 1955, has had a normal cab added! (L. W. Perkins)

Burley Quarries. A nice variety of motive power outside the locomotive shed on 11th May 1962. Left to right are *PATRICK* (AB 1887) cut-down *JUPITER* (HL 2604) and 33 (AB 1059). Watkins Gorse can be seen in the background.

(Ivo Peters)

empties, the average load taken up the bank being twelve wagons, but more were sometimes taken if extra locomotive help was available. Spending most of her time away from the yard and clamps, *BERYL* was much cleaner than the other locomotives. Calcining was discontinued in 1957 and the skip wagons broken up; the raw ironstone was then loaded into railway wagons at the quarry face, with two locomotives sharing this duty, and *BERYL* continuing the 'main line' run.

From September 1957 the quarries came under the ownership of the United Steel Companies, bringing about a rather curious situation, with the Burley tramway running side by side for most of its length with the Exton Park tramway. The sight to the casual observer on the Oakham road bridge probably seemed odd; before 1957 the two lines looked different — different track, different liveried locomotives, different coloured ore for different destinations. All this was now changed and it was easy to predict simplification of the transport system. According to a plan in the BSC archives, United Steels originally intended to retain both outlets to the Cottesmore branch, with full trains using the Exton Park connection and the empties coming up the Burley line, with a facing connection from the latter to the Exton Park line immediately east of the Oakham road bridge; the rest of the Burley system was to be lifted and a lorry road put in from the quarry to a point on the Exton Park system just beyond the loco. shed. The system adopted was the complete opposite, involving the abandonment of the Burley line from Watkin's Gorse to BR, but retaining the quarry layout; and for a couple of years Burley carried on effectively as before. By this time working had reached the northeast corner of the lease, an area east of the stream, which the tramway crossed by a bridge from a reversing point to the south. The area quarried was extended from the very small section covered by the Dorman Long lease into the adjoining ground, which was part of United Steel's Exton lease, and noted as Exton West No. 1. Production at this new layout commenced in 1959, with a 37RB diesel shovel transferred from Cottesmore.

At the takeover by United Steels, there were five locomotives — the Hawthorn Leslie *JUPITER* and four Barclays, *PATRICK*, *BERYL*, *33* and *5*, but the last was cut up later the same year; all four were kept busy much of the time and to help out a Yorkshire Engine was transferred from Exton Park early in 1959. She was a six-wheeler, as were all Exton locomotives, and the idea was that she should work all the way from quarry to BR instead of having an intermediate change at the yard; this she did, hauling 27 empties against *BERYL'S* 14, with two Barclays working the pit. It does seem extraordinary, though, that the locomotive selected for the job was

33, duplicating a number already existing at Burley, where they were referred to as 'new *33*' and 'old *33*' respectively. Not that there was much likelihood of confusion really except possibly on paper. Since the cessation of calcining the Burley stock was a bit cleaner than hitherto, but for a while 'new *33*' stood out like the proverbial silver spoon in a sootbag; but she soon lost her pristine gloss.

Only light repairs were carried out at Burley, locomotives requiring heavy overhaul being treated at Exton Park; 'old *33*' went thither in 1960 and returned in March 1961, when 'new *33*' and *BERYL* went to Exton Park. By then a scheme for full integration of the two systems had been decided; the pointwork and first few lengths of connecting line were in position at the Burley end in March 1961, the line entering Exton Park premises behind the locomotive shed. It should be mentioned that in the days of independence there was a narrow bank of untouched ironstone between the two systems, and this had been removed, hedge as well; the connection was completed about August 1961. In March and April 1961 the four remaining 'Dorman Long' locomotives were numbered 1366-69 in the new USC series, but retained their earlier identities of name or number; the new numbers were in black on a yellow disc on the rear of the bunker. They also kept their original liveries, *BERYL* and *JUPITER* remaining plain green, whereas from this time the apple green USC locomotives were being repainted in the new maroon livery.

It was however Burley's swansong, for within a year the quarry was closed and the stock summarily disposed of. Production at Burley ceased in July 1962; *JUPITER* and 'old *33*' were cut up on the spot the previous month, while *BERYL* and *PATRICK* were stored in the shed until taken in October 1962 to Colsterworth shops and cut up there. 'New *33*' was being repainted in the shed at the time of the closure and this policy continued for a while, locomotives from Exton Park being sent here for painting in succession, 1360/57/64/52/54; away from the bustle of the working environment, the painting could more satisfactorily be carried out. When all the locomotives had been painted in the new livery, the shed was sold in the autumn of 1963 to Burley Estates, when it was used for storing farm equipment. The quarry area was restored to agricultural use, and there was no further working at Exton West.

Lifting of superfluous track had commenced in June 1962 with the section between the level crossing on the Ashwell road and the headshunt west of Watkin's Gorse; the section between the level crossing and the BR junction followed, lifting being completed by the end of November. The connection to Exton Park via Watkin's Gorse, with access to the loco. shed

Burley Quarries. When United Steels took over the Burley Quarries in 1957, they soon got rid of the small locomotives and allocated one of their Yorkshire Engines to Burley. Strangely, they chose 33 — and there was already a 33 at Burley! 11th May 1962.

(Ivo Peters)

and quarry, was left, but was lifted from the immediate vicinity of the shed when Burley Estates took over. The course of the line from the headshunt was filled with earth up to field level, to a point just short of the Oakham road bridge, where the old narrow gauge shops were still intact; this was done at the end of 1962. The Midland Railway signals protecting the now vanished Ashwell Road level crossing were dismantled in the Spring of 1963 and the fields south of the crossing were fully levelled and restored to agriculture. There was track in the road still in 1964 but two years later this had gone, leaving just a mark in the tarmac, with wheat growing over the course of the line both here and east of the Oakham road. The buildings by the latter road were abandoned, the bridge filled in and the parapets demolished.

In spite of the closure of Burley quarry, there was no further track-lifting after the end of 1963 until the end of 1967, when the connecting line was lifted. The route through Watkin's Gorse was filled to its original level, while some more felling widened the gap between the trees still further, and the ends were fenced off. Today there are few remains of the Burley

Burley Quarries. When United Steels took over the Burley quarries, they put in a connection to the Exton Park system near the loco. shed, and the separate line to Cottesmore sidings was taken up. The view, looking towards Flint's Covert, on 1st July 1962, shows the dismantlement in progress, and includes the MR signal that protected the level crossing. (G. Ordish)

Burley Quarries. The locomotive shed was a fine building and remained for farm use after closure. The slight difference in the brickwork of the rearward extension can still be made out. 7th April 1984.   (Eric Tonks)

system other than the locomotive shed, a fine monument, visible over a wide area but accessible only by farm tracks. It is still in use as a store for farming purposes, and has hardly been altered a scrap; the huge doors with hinges to match, the lifting tackle at the rear, a section of rail, are still there. One outbuilding still remains — the former said drier. To the southeast is a larch plantation on the site of the former calcine bank, and the ground nearby is deep red from the calcined ore (1984); east of this is the stream with two bridges only a few yards apart, the southern one being that used by the tramway to reach the final workings. From this bridge a replacement hawthorn hedge within two wire fences shows that quarrying has taken place, and there is a dip at the final gullet, beyond which the hedge is an old one with trees. Further to the north are other single replacement hedges. The older quarrying areas towards the Oakham and Burley Bushes roads are indicated by replacement hedges and the lower level of the ground. The swathe through Watkin's Gorse shows where the rails once ran but there are no traces other than bits of purple calcine here and there, and the course of the line to the Oakham road and beyond to the reversing point has been almost completely obliterated. The course of the narrow gauge line from Oakham road to Flint's Covert was still quite clear in the 1950s, also the concrete base of the tipping stage and the pit of the locomotive shed. Today all that can be seen of the narrow gauge site is an opening in the trees in Flint's Covert and by the hedge higher up the hill, where the cutting filling seems to have subsided and exposed the ironstone. The swathe left by the standard gauge line in Flint's Covert also remains but no trace of the route towards the Ashwell road, where the level crossing site now has ordinary farm gates on the Burley side.

Grid References

885140	Junction with Cottesmore Branch
886136	Level crossing of Ashwell road
887126	Transhipment point at Flint's Covert (narrow gauge tramway)
889121	Reversing point of std gauge tramway
892127	Narrow gauge locomotive shed
894127	Bridge under Oakham road
900126	Watkin's Gorse cutting — north end
902122	Standard gauge locomotive shed
905121	Bridge over stream
905122	Final gullet
898110	Southernmost point (Burley Bushes road)

Locomotives

Gauge; 3ft. 0in.

BURLEY	0-4-0ST	OC	MW	1974	1919	8 x 14in.	2ft.4in.	New 9/1919		(1)
-	0-4-2ST	OC	KS	4066	1920	9 x 15in.	2ft.6in.	(a)		(2)
-	0-4-0ST	Oc	WB	2084	1919	7 x 12in.	1ft.9½in.	(b)		(3)

(a) ex Robert Bredin, Blaen-y-cwm Reservoir, Brecon
(b) ex Dorman Long & Co Ltd, Port Clarence, c 2/1925

(1) to Hayes, dealer, Stockport 1926; later to Nelson Corporation, Coldwell Reservoir Construction
(2) Rebuilt to 4ft. 8½in. gauge 1930
(3) to Consett Iron Co Ltd, Buttsfield Quarry, Durham c 5/1929

Gauge; 4ft. 8½in.

	NORMANBY	?		?		?	?		(a)		s/s
	ANGELA										
	(24 to 1939)	0-4-0ST	OC	AE	1793	1918	14 x 20in.	3ft.3in.	(b)		(1)
1366	PATRICK	0-4-0ST	OC	AB	1887	1926	15 x 24in.	3ft.7in.	New 3/1926		(2)
	'ADAM'	0-6-0ST	OC	VF	422	1858	16 x 24in.	4ft.0in.	(c)		Scr 1935
					Reb Caerphilly 1884, 1903						
	-	0-4-2ST	OC	KS	4066	1920			(d)		s/s
	EUNICE										
	(13 to 1939)	0-4-0ST	OC	AB	857	1899	16 x 24in.	3ft.7in.	(e)		Scr c 1944
1367	BERYL										
	(16 to 1939)	0-4-0ST	OC	AB	926	1902	16 x 24in.	3ft.7in.	(f)		(2)
1369	JUPITER (170)	0-4-0ST	OC	HL	2604	1905	14 x 22in.	3ft.6in.	(g)		Scr 6/1962
1368	33	0-4-0ST	OC	AB	1059	1905	14 x 22in.	3ft.5in.	(h)		Scr 6/1962
	EUNICE	0-4-0ST	OC	AB	1224	1911	14 x 22in.	3ft.5in.	(i)		Scr 4/1957
5		0-4-0ST	OC	AB	1515	1917	16 x 24in.	3ft.7in.	(j)		Scr 12/1957
33		0-6-0ST	OC	YE	2502	1951	18 x 24in.	3ft.8in.	(k)		(3)

(a) ex ?
(b) ex Bell Bros Ltd, Port Clarence 1920
(c) ex Dorman Long & Co Ltd, Carlton Ironworks, c 1926. (f. Rhymney Railway 10)
(d) Rebuilt from 3ft. gauge, 1930
(e) ex Dorman Long & Co Ltd, Port Clarence, 1937
(f) ex Port Clarence 1937, via Cleveland Works
(g) ex Cleveland Works 9/1940
(h) ex Acklam Works 8/1949
(i) ex Cleveland Works 9/1950
(j) ex Acklam Works 4/1954
(k) ex Exton Park Quarries 1959

(1) to Dorman Long & Co Ltd, Dean & Chapter Colliery, Co. Durham c 1946
(2) to Colsterworth East Quarries, for scrap 10/1962
(3) to Exton Park Quarries 3/1961

Quarry Machines

No.4	SND Transporter	RH	545	1919			New 7/1919		s/s
No. 8	S. Navvy	RH	554	1919			New 7/1919		s/s
37RB	D. Shovel	RB						(a)	s/s
43RB	D. Shovel	RB	18353	1954	1½ Cu.Yds.	60ft.	New 9/1954		(1)
1022 5W	E. Walking Dragline	RB	12188	1949	4 Cu.Yds.	135ft.		(b)	s/s
1103 37RB	D. Shovel	RB	4045	1939	1½ Cu.Yds.	27ft.		(c)	s/s

(a) ?
(b) ex Exton Park Quarries c 1956
(c) ex Cottesmore Quarries c 1963

(1) to Cottesmore Quarries

EXTON PARK QUARRIES

Owners: United Steel Cos Ltd Ore Mining Branch; British Steel Corporation Midland Group from 1st July 1968; British Steel Corporation, General Steels Division, Appleby Frodingham Works, from 29th March 1970.

Exton Park was the last ironstone quarrying area in the Midlands to be developed as a separate undertaking, and was of a magnitude in keeping with the accent on large-scale operations increasingly pursued in the years following World War II. The presence of beds of ore had long been known (for instance, J. W. Judd, in his *Geology of Rutland*, 1874, p.97, refers to their existence 'north of the boathouse, Exton Park') but developments had been hampered by the considerable distance from any railway, even the Cottesmore branch. The extent of the deposits was however considered by United Steels to be sufficient to justify the heavy capital expenditure. The proposals were necessarily on an ambitious scale and met with much local opposition, but eventually the company obtained the required authority, with a lease from the landowner, the Earl of Gainsborough; and in December 1948 stripping of turf for the sidings was commenced.

The standard gauge tramway layout, though extensive (it was the third largest in the country, exceeded only by Corby and Oxfordshire Ironstone) was essentially simple and it is clear that great pains were taken to make operations as inoffensive to the environment as possible. The ironstone occurred practically over the whole extent of the park and it was planned to lay a line on the perimeter, making a complete circuit, out of sight in deep cutting most of the way, and the ironstone exposed on the inner face of the cutting was to be worked inwards; a dragline to remove the overburden and a shovel to load the ironstone were the essentials of the quarry equipment. The length of the tramway, and the roughly circular layout of the main portion, made it unique and always an interesting system to observe in action. As mentioned under the Cottesmore section, the standard gauge tramway followed the course of the former narrow gauge Cottesmore line for about half a mile, enabling the Cottesmore South pit to be served en route, though the new line was designed primarily to tap reserves further east under thicker cover.

The line left the Cottesmore branch between the junction of the Burley line and the Cottesmore tippler and in the triangle between here and the

Cottesmore-Ashwell road was laid out an extensive marshalling yard with eight sidings abreast; the road was crossed on the level parallel with the Burley level crossing, with a crossing of main-line standard with gates, a keeper's box and a small signal on each side. Beyond the road was a further loop and the line (of chaired track on wooden sleepers and earth ballast) then climbed steadily at 1 in 50 to the bridge under the Cottesmore-Oakham road formerly used by the narrow gauge line but now enlarged to take standard gauge tracks and relined with brick. A further series of reception sidings (five tracks) for trains coming down from the quarries and empties from the junction were laid out on level ground and a commodious two-road engine shed and other offices in white precast blocks was situated here; a branch to Cottesmore South pit turned off by the shed, and beyond this point the line singled again and then divided into the two principal branches to workings in the park. The junction was in cutting and the north branch running along the perimeter of the park followed the contour and lay in cutting for the whole distance as far as Fort Henry on the shores of the pool; the apparent depth of the rather sombre cutting was enhanced by the irregular heaps of spoil lining the banks. The line passed beneath the Greetham road by a concrete tunnel and about a mile from here an auxiliary water supply for locomotives was provided, consisting of

Exton Park Quarries. An everyday scene, with a Yorkshire Engine 16in. locomotive ascending the bank up the Oolitic escarpment with a train of empties for the quarry. July 1962. (G. P. Roberts)

Exton Park Quarries. The locomotive shed, 13th January 1962. The building of precast blocks and corrugated asbestos was later acquired by Davro Fabrications Ltd.

(R. K. Hateley)

Exton Park Quarries. The northern line to Fort Henry, looking east, on 5th May 1953. Note ironstone 'bench' on right. The line was laid so as to minimise encroachment on woodland, and was in cutting for much of the route, so that the vista over the park was unimpeded. (BGS)

a diesel-driven pump for raising water from a stream. The track was flat-bottomed on wooden sleepers, with occasional steel tie-bars, but points were chaired. At Fort Henry the line emerged into the open to cross a farm track by a level crossing.

Quarrying commenced on this section pending the completion of the full circular route, the other half of which commenced to rise immediately beyond the junction east of the office area and, turning south, ran chiefly on the surface of the ground apart from one high embankment over a little valley between (delightful names!) Rattling Jack Spinney and Cocked Hat Spinney. The southern line was laid almost to main-line standards, with chaired track on steel or wooden sleepers set in deep ballast, some of them new and some ex LMSR, SR and Metropolitan Railway; the line was of course a permanent route as far as a point beyond Exton village and not subject to any movement for quarrying. The line crossed on the level the splendid mile length of Barnsdale Avenue and two minor roads to Exton village; these crossings were at first ungated but in 1955 gates and keepers' boxes were erected in expectation of regular traffic when the nine-mile

Exton Park Quarries. View of the northern line looking west. The parapet of the Greetham road bridge can be seen in the distance. 5th May 1953. (B G S)

circuit was completed in 1956. The gates were electrically operated from the cabins, with equipment supplied by the Railway Signal Co Ltd. A sub-station supplying power for the quarry machines was situated by the Barnsdale Avenue crossing. The output during the early 1950s was some 10,000 tons per week, and more than that when the line was fully operational; the round trip from Cottesmore Gorse Exchange Sidings was about twelve miles. The reserves were estimated to be sufficient for 80-90 years.

In the first stages of construction, materials were brought up to the Cottesmore branch and placed by the BR locomotive as required, but soon after the level crossing had been completed a locomotive was sent from Colsterworth; this was *No. 34*, built by Kitson to Manning Wardle designs, and during the construction period she was stabled in the sidings by the Ashwell road. New locomotives were ordered from the Yorkshire Engine Co (of the United Steel Cos group) and these were ready for service when production commenced in November 1951. They were six-coupled, as were all locomotives at Exton Park, and were painted in a very attractive livery of apple green lined dark Brunswick green edged with yellow, with red coupling rods and lettering in gold *UNITED STEEL COMPANIES LTD, ORE MINING BRANCH* on the tanks and *EXTON PARK* on the bunkers. Numbers were either in gold paint or in cast brass; amongst the latter it can

Exton Park Quarries. The first locomotive on the site was this Kitson built to Manning Wardle design. She came from Scunthorpe and is here shown in the shed on 23rd September 1954. Soon afterwards she was moved to Cringle quarries. (G. Alliez. Courtesy B. D. Stoyel)

be noted that 33 had flat-topped 3s and 36 a round-topped 3. An unusual feature of the design was the cab, curved inwards at the top in the manner of the SR 'Schools'. Just before full-circle working began, three new locomotives were ordered from Yorkshire Engine Co, but these were of the famous 'Austerity' pattern that had been introduced in World War II at the behest of the Ministry of Supply and based on an existing Hunslet design. The new engines also had a different but equally smart livery of maroon lined yellow and black, with *ORE MINING BRANCH* carried on red-backed

Exton Park Quarries. Nearly all the work in the quarries was performed by locomotives built by Yorkshire Engine Co Ltd, a company in the United Steels group. The earlier ones had 16in. cylinders. That shown is 39, YE 2483. 4th April 1960.

(S. A. Leleux)

Exton Park Quarries. 36, YE 2489, in the shed at Exton Park. Some of the locomotives had cast brass numerals. 23rd September 1954. (G. Alliez. Courtesy B. D. Stoyel)

Exton Park Quarries. The last steam locomotives at Exton Park were built by Yorkshire Engine Co Ltd. 11, YE 2568, poses at the beautiful Barnsdale Avenue level crossing on 7th May 1955. (S. Cartwright)

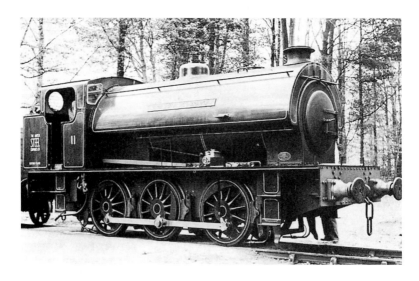

plates on the tank and the USC totem and *EXTON PARK* in small block letters (yellow, shaded black) on the bunker. A fourth 'Austerity' was obtained in 1961, similarly painted but with *EXTON PARK* in larger block letters. In practice the 'Austerities' were more prone to trouble than the 16in. locomotives because of their steel fireboxes.

The apparently erratic numbering scheme arose from the allocation of numbers to locomotives and other machines in one series, with blanks being filled as they fell vacant. An anomaly arose with the 'Austerities', allotted 40 to 42 when ordered in 1954; when the locomotives were delivered in 1955, these numbers had been given to quarry machines and the engines became 10 to 12 by chipping off the relevant portions of the brass numerals. The locomotives were all fitted with mechanical lubricators and were exceedingly well kept; the 16in. machines had rocking grates, which made for easier ash disposal, but not the 18in. 'Austerities'.

One piece of rolling stock unusual for an industrial system was an eight-seat inspection car built by the Drewry Car Co Ltd and obtained from BR; this was painted in the earlier standard USC livery of green with red and yellow lining. It was intended for taking personnel over the lengthy system, but lack of passing places prevented its being used very much; from 1954 it was housed in a separate brick shed east of the main locomotive shed. There were a few specialised wagons; a bogie well wagon, No. 1 (later given plant number 1406) for carrying heavy machinery, and two flat wagons lettered *UNITED STEEL COMPANIES ORE MINING BRANCH, EXTON PARK No. 1* and *No. 2*, painted in white on grey; they were built by Metropolitan Cammell Carriage & Wagon Co

Exton Park Quarries. Well wagon used for carrying heavy quarry equipment, by the loco. shed. 1st December 1973. (Eric Tonks)

103

Exton Park Quarries. Giant W 1400 dragline shortly before entering service, 1957. Main tramway to left. (BSC)

Ltd, Midland Works. There was also a flat wooden wagon built by S. J. Claye Ltd of Long Eaton, and with a plate 'General Repair, L.N.W.R. 27702'. For carrying ore, standard railway wagons were used throughout from quarry to blast furnace; these were 27-ton 'tipplers' and 21-22 ton hoppers. Unlike Burley, no calcining was done, and the ore went almost entirely to Scunthorpe.

The quarry machines were not numerous, as there were not many faces; but throughout the main operating period the scene was dominated by the huge W1400 Ransomes & Rapier dragline, at the time of its erection the largest excavator in the world, with a 282-foot boom and a 32-ton capacity bucket. It carried the name *SUNDEW*, the Grand National winner in the year (1957) the machine was put into service. At Cottesmore South a 5W walking dragline was used for removing overburden and a 100RB for loading. A 5W was also used to open up the northern gullet in the period 1952-55 and the south gullet in 1955-56. The original intention was to work inwards both from north and south but in the event the stone on the north side was found to be inferior, and the W 1400, which had been sent

Exton Park Quarries. Cottesmore south quarry, with 5W walking dragline removing and levelling overburden. 100RB shovel in pit. This view was taken in 1951, shortly after the replacement of the narrow gauge line from Cottesmore. (A. R. Crawford)

there to commence operations in earnest, was transferred to the south face and spent the rest of its working life at Exton there, with a standard 100 RB for loading. The original target of 10,000 tons per week — 5000 from each face — was achieved from the one face only.

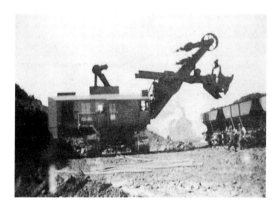

Exton Park Quarries. Cottesmore South quarry, with 100RB shovel loading hopper wagons. In the background is a 16in. YE locomotive waiting to take the train to the sidings. (RRM Archives)

105

The first output came from the northern line, as this tapped ironstone in the course of construction; when in 1955 the southern line had been laid beyond the Exton crossing, production commenced on this side also and there were then four locomotives in daily use — one on each quarry branch and two working between the loco. shed sidings and the BR branch terminus. A specially fine sight was that of two engines — one at the front and one at the rear — lifting a train of empties up the Cliff, the double blast echoing across the Vale. One of these latter locomotives probably also worked Cottesmore South pit. From 1956, when the full circle was in operation, it was usual to have four locomotives working the circuit and one handling the bank; each locomotive made three trips daily with six wagons (16in. locos) or seven wagons (18in. locos) under normal conditions, but more or fewer as required by demand. The locomotive allocated to work the bank took fourteen wagons or fifteen (for 16in. and 18in. machines respectively) and wagon brakes were pinned for the descent.

Exton Park Quarries. A YE diesel locomotive stands while its train of tipplers is being loaded by a 100RB shovel in Exton Park. The heavy overburden of Lincolnshire Limestone will be noted. This was taken nearly at the end of operations, 5th April 1972. (N. L. Cadge)

Exton Park Quarries. The Exton Park locomotives were always immaculately turned out. Originally they were painted apple green, lined with dark green and yellow. This one is 27 (YE 2501), as on 1st September 1952. (Ken Cooper/IRS Collection)

Work at Cottesmore South pit continued even after the full circuit was completed and up to 1962; it had been operated fairly intensively, over nearly all the ground bounded by the Cottesmore-Burley and Cottesmore-Barnsdale roads north of the main tramway, to the outskirts of the village. It was planned to extend the workings further east, a step involving the demolition of Cottesmore House and the realignment of the road from Cottesmore village to the tramway bridge on a parallel course to the east while the ore was obtained from under the original road; this plan was not however implemented except for the incursion of the final workface into the grounds at the rear of Cottesmore House, which was later burnt out (no connection with quarrying...!)

In September 1957 the adjacent Burley quarries of Dorman Long & Co Ltd were acquired by USC and in due course were connected to the Exton Park system by a line opened for traffic in October 1961; but the Burley quarries were closed in July 1962 (see under the Burley heading for fuller details). The Burley locomotive stock was integrated with that of Exton Park—numerically speaking—but there were few similarities between Burley's workaday four-wheelers and Exton Park's rather splendid six-

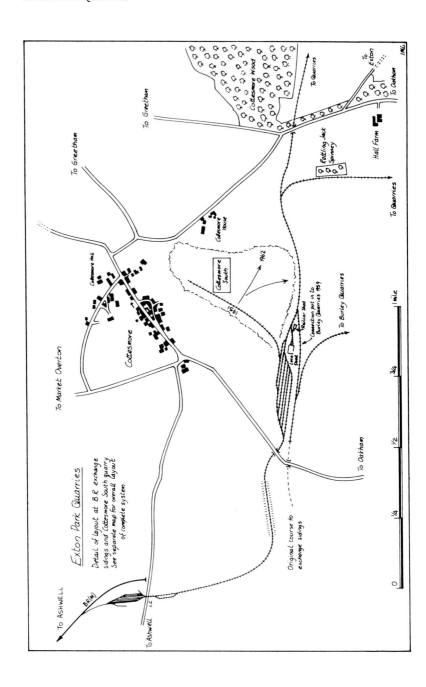

Exton Park Quarries

Detail of layout at B.R. exchange sidings and Cottesmore South quarry. See separate map for overall layout of complete system.

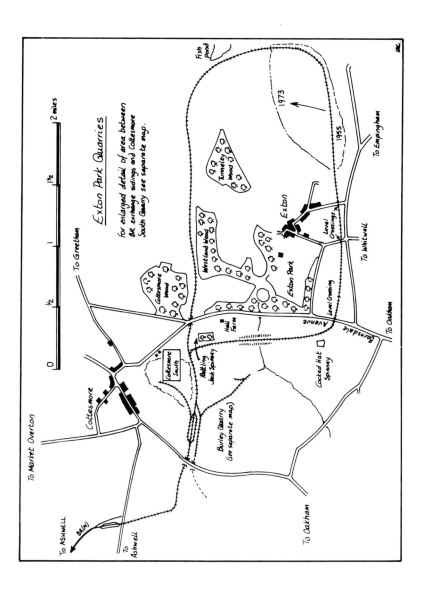

wheelers; and when Burley pit was closed the whole stock was summarily despatched. For a time Burley shed was used for the repainting of Exton Park's 16in. locomotives in the new maroon livery and to complete the renumbering scheme introduced in October 1960, in which ore Mining Branch locomotives (Colsterworth, Exton Park and Burley) were numbered 1351 upwards in the same order as the existing numbers. The new livery was maroon, lined black edged on the inside with yellow, and the words *ORE MINING BRANCH OF THE UNITED STEEL COMPANIES LTD* painted on the tanks in yellow, shaded with green, and *EXTON PARK* in similar serif letters on the cabsides. The new numbers were painted in black on a yellow circle on the bunkers or cab back. 1356/7/60/4 were repainted at Burley, 1362 at Colsterworth. Locomotives usually faced uphill on the bank, but 1352 faced the other way; the last was also repainted at Burley, but was always in maroon livery.

From July 1962 operations were concentrated on the Exton Park circuit, Cottesmore South and Burley by then being finished. In 1962 another development on the transport side was mooted, this time from BR, who suggested that United Steels might consider taking over the working of the Cottesmore branch, i.e. the exchange point to be at Ashwell sidings

Exton Park Quarries. From the early 1960s the locomotives were given an equally smart livery of maroon, lined yellow and black. This one is 1357 (in the new numbering) but the same locomotive, YE 2501. (Ken Cooper/IRS Collection)

Exton Park Quarries. Displaced by well kept and highly efficient diesel locomotives, the last three steamers lie abandoned on the spur of the connection to Burley quarry, their woebegone condition heightened by the gorse and willowherb surrounding them. 8th August 1967. (M. J. Leah)

instead of at Cottesmore Gorse. As we shall see, BR proposed a somewhat different scheme at Market Overton, but again designed to simplify BR workings and to reduce freight charges to the ironstone operators. Trials were made over the branch, with two 'Austerities' taking trains of up to 40 wagons (a locomotive at each end) to Ashwell sidings. This apparently was accomplished easily enough, but it did mean extended shifts for the crews and the idea was never taken up.

The next development was the introduction of diesel power, which was done in characteristic efficient 'no nonsense' fashion. The first was the almost brand-new 200hp Yorkshire Engine 0-6-0DE from United Steel's Easton mine near Colsterworth, which came for trials at the beginning of 1961, but was found to be insufficiently powered. Then came an eight-coupled diesel hydraulic of the Yorkshire Engine Co's 'Taurus' class on demonstration on 2nd June 1962, but evidently did not find favour, possibly because of the curve on the bank up to the Oakham road and elsewhere. Two diesels, one of 400hp and one of 440hp, were sent from Frodingham in June 1964 for trial purposes; the smaller one was found not be powerful enough, but the larger machine did the work satisfactorily and was joined by two similar locomotives in April 1965, with a further one a year later. Steam was eliminated almost from the moment the three diesels took over, though for a short time one of the 'Austerities' continued to work the section between the marshalling sidings and the level crossing. 1356/60 — a mere eleven years old and in tip-top condition — were cut up; 1363/4, with copper fireboxes, were to be kept but in fact only 1364 saw any further service. Three of the 'Austerities' were kept as standbys but were officially withdrawn from service in November 1965, and in 1966 were relegated to the spur of the connecting line to Burley, and were cut up there. The diesels had a livery similar to the steamers — maroon lined yellow (inner) and black (outer); they carried the 'plant numbers' in the 13XX series in black on yellow circular panels, but retained the original solid brass numbers DE5 etc below the cab windows.

There were no essential changes in the operating pattern, with three locomotives working the circuit and one between marshalling sidings and the BR branch terminus; the normal load on the circuit was ten wagons,and from early 1965 a similar loading was imposed down the bank. This followed a runaway when a twenty-wagon train descending the bank became out of control; fortunately the sidings were empty and the points set for the branch, along which the train proceeded quite a distance before coming to a halt, with no damage done and no-one hurt. Up the bank trains of thirty empties were handled (even 44 on one occasion, it was said,

Exton Park Quarries. Locomotive DE 7 taking loaded wagons into the BR sidings over the Ashwell Road level crossing. 2nd June 1966. Note crossing gates and keeper's hut.

(G. H. Starmer)

Exton Park Quarries. Locomotive DE 7 starts the long haul up the bank south of the level crossing, with 40 wagons. 2nd June 1966. (G. H. Starmer)

though this was contrary to instructions). At the BR sidings the wagons were usually pulled into the sidings but sometimes the locomotive ran round the train by the loop on the east side of the crossing, and then propelled the train. This was dictated by conditions in the sidings, and it was sometimes the practice for the BR diesel to propel the empties from Ashwell yard, with brakevans at the front.

By 1970 the main working face at the Exton (south east) end of the circuit had moved considerably towards the centre of the park, and the line had been slewed obliquely across in a more or less direct line between Fort Henry and the eastern level crossing by Exton village. Cutbacks or rationalisation in ironstone production, and closure of quarries, abounded throughout the 1960s; Exton Park carried on but the implementation of the BSC 'Anchor Scheme' at Scunthorpe, based on imported ore, spelt the deathknell of the last major usage of British ironstone outside Corby. By the end of 1971 production was down to 5000 tons per week and the last working face (No. 7 Face, officially) being close to the Exton end of the circuit, it was decided to abandon circular working and to operate the quarry as most other quarries were, at the end of a single branch. Outwards as well as inward, trains travelled via the southern section, thereby saving about two miles per trip, and allowing the surplus rail to be lifted. A pair of rails on the northern section by the bridge was lifted 12th January 1972, but no further lifting was done for some time, the track becoming steadily more overgrown, with water plants invading the sections where seeping occurred. Some track also remained in Cottesmore South pit, where work had long since ceased; the line here, too, was either waterlogged or overgrown. Operating was less efficient on the truncated system, obviously; instead of getting access to the loader immediately the previous train had left, trains now had to wait in the loops by Rattling Jack Spinney and near the quarry entrance, until the road was clear; loaded trains had the right of way. All four locomotives were used, but only 120 wagons were loaded per day instead of 160 when the circuit was operated. The round trip took about 2½ hours and crews had no official break, eating their meals in the cab when in sidings or loops; hours were 6.30am to 5.0pm.

Closure was planned for June 1972, in the expectation that the 'Anchor Scheme' at Scunthorpe would be operational by then, but delays with the latter ensured the continuation of operations at Exton Park for almost another year. In April 1973 the quarries were temporarily closed as a result of a strike at the Scunthorpe works; Colsterworth quarries did not reopen after the strike, but Exton Park did and the last train left the quarry at 3.0pm on

Tuesday 29th May 1973. During the steelworks strike the men at Exton Park were employed lifting track on the northern section of the loop, since this could be done without prejudicing any resumption of operations, and lifting of this section was completed in September 1973. Lifting of the southern section began just before this (by 1st September the track ended at the first level crossing by Exton village) and continued rapidly; by 1st December the track had been lifted to just east of the locomotive shed. Some of the sidings had been lifted but a through route to BR was left in. Up to then, most of the material had been despatched by rail, but now the sleepers were piled in the works yard to be picked up by lorries. The locomotives had gone one by one in the second half of 1973, the last being 1395, which left the week before Christmas; they found fresh employment at Normanby Park steelworks.

During January 1974 track was lifted between the loco. shed yard to just beyond the Oakham road bridge, but the BSC gang under foreman G. Rose (who had been responsible for laying the narrow gauge line to Cottesmore South some 33 years earlier, and some of the standard gauge lines) finished on Friday, 8th February 1974, leaving the remaining track down to Cottesmore sidings to be lifted by contractors. By this time, restoration of the quarry area had been completed, and filling in of the northern branch commenced, working back from Fort Henry. The remaining restoration was carried out in a desultory but nonetheless ultimately thorough fashion. The track from Ashwell road level crossing to Oakham road bridge was still intact in July 1974, very rusty and overgrown, but the saplings at the top of the incline were being cut down as a prelude to lifting, and by November everything had gone, level crossing gates and cabin included; the cutting near the summit remained but had been smoothed over, later to become Leicestershire County Council's 'Cottesmore Waste Disposal Site' — still in operation in 1980. By the autumn of 1975 the restoration had been virtually completed. The final working face was incorporated into the fields as a steep but cultivatable slope, and can easily be seen from the trackway to Fort Henry; the line towards the Exton level crossing was likewise restored with a 'cliff' on one side, while at Fort Henry the ground was levelled up and planted with trees. The course of the northern line was completely filled in and levelled; the parapets of the bridge on the Greetham road remain but are filled beneath and the fields each side show no trace of the line. On the southern line the level crossing gates with the lane to Exton village have gone, but a fence remains along the north side of the former trackbed; at Barnsdale Avenue the substation is still present. Of the trackbed by Rattling Jack Spinney there is no trace at all; the embankment over the stream to the south has gone but the vegetation on the site of it is different and even under snow it can be picked out by its darker colour.

As with Burley, the most tangible remains are the locomotive shed and the buildings grouped round it, which were acquired in 1976 by Davro Fabrications Ltd, a firm making welding equipment; the concrete road from the Oakham road is still present as access, and beyond the shed the trackbed extends about a quarter of a mile and from the end, beyond which the ground has been restored to original level, can be seen the terminal face of Cottesmore South pit. This continues as a long S-shaped water-filled gullet to a point just beyond the site of Cottesmore House; a little filling at the end, by Bullivant of South Witham, took place from 1978 onwards — a pity, as it was a delightful 'reserve' for the naturalist. On the worked-out portion of Cottesmore South pit towards the Oakham road, single hedges of hawthorn abound and the ground level has been lowered generally over most of the area. East of the Oakham road bridge is a section of cutting that in 1980 was described as a 'Civic Amenity Tip', for the reception of domestic refuse in skips. The parapets of red brick with squares and rectangles of blue brick and concrete top remain on the east side only; the west side was demolished in the winter of 1979/80 and replaced by a fence.

The most notable event of the closure was undoubtedly the highly publicised overland 'walk' of the W1400 dragline *SUNDEW* from Exton Park to Shotley quarry of the Corby systems in 1974. This spectacular exercise, calling for rigorously detailed planning, not to say a great deal of confidence, has been described in some quarters as a stunt, but in fact was undertaken for sound commercial reasons. It was estimated that to dismantle this colossal machine into transportable parts and re-erect it at Corby would take three years; walking would require only that many months, and the compensation to landowners and payment for services to local authorities would be only a fraction of the cost of the dismantling. It was not even necessary to remove the boom, as this balanced the machine. So the great move was carried out between 10th June and 5th August 1974[1]; the hardest part was choosing the route to give the least disturbance. In all, ten roads and four rivers, one main railway line and 74 hedges were crossed, at an average speed of one mile per ten hours; there was a break half way when the six-mile cable was transferred from Exton to Corby. And so *SUNDEW* came to Corby with the naive message 'Excuse me; I'm walking to Corby' painted on the body.

There were two enthusiast railtours of Exton Park, one steam-hauled

Exton Park Quarries.
Cottesmore South pit
behind the site of the
demolished Cottesmore
House, looking towards
the terminus. 5th
September 1977.

(Eric Tonks)

before the circle was completed, on 7th May 1955 and another, diesel-hauled, after the circle had been severed, on 24th June 1972. The first tour was organised by the Birmingham Locomotive Club and on it 'Austerity' 11 hauled two wagonloads of enthusiasts, with suitable stops for photography; the later tour was organised by the Railway Correspondence & Travel Society, this time with four wagons, with diesels 1393 and 1395, one at each end of the train, and emphasising the great rise in popularity of industrial railtours.

Exton Park Quarries. *SUNDEW* pauses on its way to Corby, July 1974. She has just crossed the Welland and now waits to cross the road near Wakerley for the last leg of the journey.   (RRM Archives/R. Dean Collection)

Footnote

1. The Great Walk, by Roy Dean (former Chief Surveyor, British Steel Corporation, Corby). Rutland Railway Museum, 1983.

Grid References

886136	Level crossing with Ashwell road
890129	Cutting west of Oakham road
894128	Bridge under Oakham road
902127	Locomotive shed
903127	Junction of circle formation
913127	Bridge under Greetham road
910119	Embankment between Rattling Jack Spinney and Cocked Hat Spinney — north end
912106	Level crossing of Barnsdale Avenue
923106	)
928107	) Level crossings by Exton village
949117	Level crossing with Fort Henry farm track
906134	Cottesmore South pit — gullet terminus
935112	Terminal gullet near Park Road

Locomotives

Gauge; 4ft. 8½in.

	No. 34	0-6-0ST	IC	K	5457	1931	12 x 18in.	3ft.0½in.	(a)	(1)
1364	No. 39	0-6-0ST	OC	YE	2483	1950	16 x 24in.	3ft.8in.	New 2/1951	(2)
1362	No. 37	0-6-0ST	OC	YE	2484	1950	16 x 24in.	3ft.8in.	New 2/1951	(3)
1361	36	0-6-0ST	OC	YE	2489	1950	16 x 24in.	3ft.8in.	New 9/1951	(4)
1357	27	0-6-0ST	OC	YE	2501	1951	16 x 24in.	3ft.8in.	New 5/1952	(5)
1360	33	0-6-0ST	OC	YE	2502	1951	16 x 24in.	3ft.8in.	New 1/1953	(6)
1356	26	0-6-0ST	OC	YE	2512	1952	16 x 24in.	3ft.8in.	New 12/1952	
									Scr 10/1964	
1351	10	0-6-0ST	IC	YE	2567	1954	18 x 26in.	4ft.0½in.	New 3/1955	
	(40 to 4/1955)								Scr 11/1967	
1352	11	0-6-0ST	IC	YE	2568	1954	18 x 26in.	4ft.0½in.	New 4/1955	
	(41 to 4/1955)								Scr 12/1967	
1353	12	0-6-0ST	IC	YE	2569	1954	18 x 26in.	4ft.0½in.	New 5/1955	(7)
	(42 to 1955)									
1354	13	0-6-0ST	IC	YE	2573	1954	18 x 26in.	4ft.0½in.	(b)	Scr 11/1967
	-	4wPMR		DC	1303	1923			(c)	Scr 1958
	-	0-6-0DE		YE	2744	1960	200 hp		(d)	(8)
	DE 1	0-6-0DE		YE	2709	1959	400 hp		(e)	(9)
1395	DE 5	0-6-0DE		YE	2791	1962	446 hp		(f)	(10)
1396	DE 6	0-6-0DE		YE	2784	1962	446 hp		(g)	(11)
1397	DE 7	0-6-0DE		YE	2897	1963	446 hp		(g)	(11)
1393	DE 3	0-6-0DE		YE	2792	1961	446 hp		(h)	(12)

(a) ex Colsterworth Quarries 11/1950
(b) ex United Coke and Chemicals Ltd, 2/1961
(c) ex British Railways, Birkenhead (formerly Mersey Railway)
(d) ex Easton Mine, Colsterworth, loan c 2/1961
(e) ex Frodingham Quarries 6/1964
(f) ex Frodingham Quarries 6/1964
(g) ex Frodingham Quarries 8/1964
(h) ex Frodingham Quarries 8/1965

(1) to Cringle Quarries 4/1956
(2) to Colsterworth Quarries 1965
(3) to Cringle Quarries 10/1955, via YE; ex Cringle 12/1956; to Cringle 3/1957; ex Colsterworth Quarries 10/1962. Scr 11/1964
(4) to Colsterworth Quarries c 7/1963
(5) to Colsterworth Quarries 1964
(6) to Burley Quarries 1959; ex Burley 3/1961. Scr 8/1964
(7) to NCB North Eastern Division, Area 6, North Gawber Colliery 1/1961; ex North Gawber 6/1961. Scr 2/1968
(8) ret. to Easton Mine c 3/1965
(9) to Frodingham Quarries 3/1965
(10) to Normanby Park steelworks 12/1973
(11) to Normanby Park steelworks 7/1973
(12) to Normanby Park steelworks 9/1973

Quarry Machines

	43RB	D. Dragline	RB					(a)	(1)
	37RB	D. Shovel	RB					(b)	(2)
	5W	E. Walking Dragline	RB	9215	1946	4 Cu.Yds.	135ft.	(c)	(3)
1022	5W	E. Walking Dragline	RB	12188	1949	4 Cu.Yds.	135ft.	New 1950	(4)
1076	100RB	E. Shovel	RB	12224	1951	3½ Cu.Yds.	32ft.	New 1951	(5)
1078	100RB	E. Shovel	RB	16280	1954	3½ Cu.Yds.	32ft.	New 3/1954	(6)
	100RB	E. Shovel	RB	16282	1954	3½ Cu.Yds.	32ft.	New 4/1954	(7)
1005	W1400	E. Walking Dragline	R&R	2625	1957	26 Cu.Yds.	282ft.	New 1957	(8)

(a) ex Cottesmore Quarries (?)
(b) ex Cottesmore Quarries (?)
(c) ex Cottesmore Quarries c 1950, when Cottesmore South quarry taken over

(1) Opening up Exton Park quarry line. s/s
(2) At Cottesmore South quarry; to Exton Park quarry. To ?, 1953
(3) At Cottesmore South quarry. Opened up Exton Park quarry. To Cottesmore South quarry 2/1952. s/s c 1963
(4) At Exton Park quarry. To Burley Quarries c 1956
(5) At Cottesmore South quarry. To Colsterworth North Quarries c 1963
(6) At Exton Park quarry. To Glendon Quarries 1974
(7) At Exton Park quarry. To Corby Quarries c 1973
(8) At Exton Park quarry. To Corby Quarries (Shotley) 6/1974

MARKET OVERTON QUARRIES

Owners: James Pain Ltd: Stanton Ironworks Co Ltd from 1st January 1928; Stewarts & Lloyds Minerals Ltd from 1st January 1950: British Steel Corporation, Tubes Division Minerals from 29th March 1970.

Quarry History

Market Overton quarries were the first outside Northamptonshire to be operated by James Pain, who from small beginnings at Desborough had greatly expanded the Glendon quarries and was looking for further areas for development; these included two in Rutland—Market Overton, opened up in 1906, and Uppingham a few years later. Market Overton village is close to the Oolitic escarpment, and the quarries were grouped round it on three sides, north, east and south; and the newly opened Saxby-Bourne line gave easy rail access, as for Buckminster, with which Market Overton was worked in conjunction in later years when they were in common ownership.

Full details of the leases acquired by Pain have not come to light, but there were three; with the Wingfield estate, the Ecclesiastical

Market Overton Quarries. The bridge under the Thistleton road leading to Nos. 4 and 5 quarries and Barrow face. Note the company houses on the road. 1951.   (B S C)

Market Overton Quarries. Sunshine and shadow etch the formal outlines of the company cottages on Thistleton Road, viewed from the rear on 7th April 1984. This area has been excavated for ironstone as 'The Parks', with a tramway connection under the road to the right of the cottages. (Eric Tonks)

Commissioners, and the Wing estate, for areas respectively north, east and southeast of Market Overton. To serve them a standard gauge tramway left the Midland Railway at 'Pains Sidings' and ran for three quarters of a mile generally southwards on a somewhat sinuous course, on a rising gradient much of the way, to the administrative centre where were located offices, locomotive sheds and other buildings. Like so many quarries opened up before the motor age, but unlike Buckminster, this area was nowhere near the road, but was connected by a bridle road with the Market Overton-Thistleton road about a mile distant. It is interesting to note that this bridle road appears in a Market Overton Award of 2nd November 1807 as a 'Public Bridle Road... for the purpose of carrying stone and other materials from the Stone Pitt'. This information was provided by Mr. W. Jones, the British Steel Corporation surveyor at Sysonby Lodge. The tramway was continued southwards, in cutting most of the way, alongside the bridleway and under Thistleton Road by a brick tunnel, so that the first two quarries could be opened up; the main one, on the Wingfield estate, lay west of the bridle way, and was worked northwards from the Thistleton road between the bridge and the church, and the other, on Glebe land, south of Thistleton Road between it and Pinfold Lane, working eastwards. Both these areas were in production from 1907 onwards, but came to an end in the smaller pit in 1911, when difficulties were met, whereupon working was continued south of Pinfold Lane as far as the Cottesmore road, in the period

121

1911-16. The tramway was extended a half mile south to a new quarry on the Wing estate, on flattish ground east of the Cottesmore road, on the edge of the present airfield, passing under Pinfold Lane and 'Back Lane' by brick tunnels. The date of commencement is not recorded, but was probably about 1917. On the south side of Thistleton Road, west of the bridge, a terrace of twelve houses was built for quarrymen.

There does not appear to be a full record of the titles of these quarries operated by James Pain, whose normal custom was to refer to his various quarry faces by name rather than by number. GSM(1920) however quotes numbers as follows: No. 1, east of Cottesmore Road, No. 2, north of Thistleton Road (Note they are not in order of opening) and a third east of the village, south of Pinfold Lane. The eastern half of No. 1 quarry, now under water, was also known as Bussack Barn, from a local landmark; while the quarries east of the village were known as 'The Parks', and GSM gives 'Park' as an alternative title to the third quarry.

Pain sold his ore on the open market, but in the 1920s trade was slack and in 1928 all his properties were acquired by Stanton Ironworks Co Ltd. 'The Parks' quarries had been closed long before, but a small area of the Cottesmore Road quarry remained, which Stanton continued to refer to as No. 1 until work ceased there early in 1930. No. 2 quarry near the headquarters was worked northwards continually from 1928 in a clockwise manner until terminated by deterioration of the stone under thicker cover in 1943. This quarry was leased from Lt. Col. Parry Wingfield. No. 3 quarry, immediately to the east of the northern section of No. 2, was commenced in 1929 on the bridleway itself and then working west to east, the bridleway being reinstated at the lower level. Work ceased in 1931, probably because of low demand, and was resumed in 1938, working northwards anti-clockwise. The stone became progressively poor however and working was abandoned in 1956, leaving a deep gullet to Thistleton Road. This ground was covered by a lease of 353½ acres from the Ecclesiastical Commissioners for 40 years from 25th March 1929.

An additional working face east of the Cottesmore road, to the north of the old No. 1 quarry, was opened in 1936 on 51 acres of ground leased from Mrs. H. S. Nottidge for 25 years from 25th March 1935, and was termed No. 4 quarry; this fairly small area was worked clockwise up to 1940. Further development on this side of Cottesmore Road was precluded by extensions to Cottesmore RAF station, but ground on the west side, opposite No. 1 quarry, was developed by virtue of a lease of 118 acres of the Wing estate, for 20 years from 25th March 1940. The tramway was extended across the Cottesmore road on the level and operations

Market Overton Quarries. 21RB long-boom dragline opening up the Barrow face in 1940. This view is looking north and the rail track turned east by the farther dragline to cross the Cottesmore road on the level. (BSC)

commenced in 1940 at the 'Barrow Face' — it never seems to have been given a number — and ended in 1948. Working was anti-clockwise from the north as far as the road to Barrow village. Stanton also purchased the freehold of about 30 acres south of this road, but this was not touched and was later re-leased to Appleby-Frodingham Steel Co Ltd and worked as part of their Cottesmore system (which see). Stanton also renewed the existing leases with the Wingfield and Wing estates through Midland Bank Executor & Trustee Co Ltd, totalling 802 acres, for 35 years from 25th March 1935, with a further 545 acres leased from Lt. Col. Parry Wingfield. There was also a much larger area (2361 acres) in the parishes of Stretton, Greetham, Thistleton, Castle Bytham and North Witham, for 59 years from 30th July 1940, leased from Major Fleetwood-Hesketh, and evidently earmarked for future development that never materialised; the lease was determined on 30th July 1970.

S. H. Beaver visited Market Overton in April 1930, i.e. very soon after it had been taken over by Stanton, and in *Rutland Record* No. 3, 1982/3, p.114, he records what he saw; by then No. 1 quarry had been closed, No. 2 was in full swing, and No. 3 was just being opened. At No. 2 quarry the cover was removed by a steam shovel and conveyor (the latter had been

Market Overton Quarries. An early (probably 1920s) postcard when steam quarry machines were a thing of wonder. The identity of this machine is not known but she appears to be working in No. 2 quarry. (RRM Archives)

brought in by Stanton) and the ore was removed by a smaller shovel; water was a nuisance in this pit, necessitating pumping. At No. 3 face the cover was removed by hand and the ore by steam shovel. The ore was sent mainly to outside customers, in continuation of Pain's policy as Stanton could obtain all their requirements more conveniently from Buckminster; these customers included Frodingham ironworks at Scunthorpe, Partington's works at Irlam and Walter Scott's at Leeds, and it is worth noting that Scunthorpe and Irlam were still taking ore from Market Overton in the 1970s.

Pain despatched ore in his own wagons, but nothing is known of them beyond the belief that they were of wood and of a brown livery. The locomotives are however well recorded and by 1910 consisted of three new Pecketts, an allocation that remained practically constant throughout Pain's period of ownership. The total was artificially doubled in 1927 by the stock from his Uppingham quarries, presumably sent here as the nearest place to Uppingham when the latter closed in 1926. In this slack period there could have been no need for the extra power, and the locomotives were soon disposed of when Stanton took over. Stanton used any locomotives in their 'pool' but the allocation in the 1930s was only two, of which *UPPINGHAM* was always one. During World War II the work increased enough to require four locomotives, but this fell to three afterwards.

James Pain was an early advocate of mechanical handling, and Market Overton was mechanised from the start; there was a 12-ton Whitaker shovel, a 15-ton Berry, and two Ruston Proctors of 12 and 20 ton types, which were moved to the different faces as required. Stanton introduced more machines, including a transporter that was used along with the Berry shovel at No. 2 quarry (by 1930) then at No. 3 quarry (by 1936); at that time the other three machines were in No. 2 quarry, but a small 8-ton Ruston Proctor machine came that year, possibly for No. 4 quarry. Two more steam machines, a Bucyrus navvy and a Ruston & Hornsby dragline, came from Buckminster; both survived World War II but had finished by 1950. The first diesel machines were small draglines—a 43RB in No. 4 quarry, a No. 4 petrol-paraffin, and a 21RB; but there was a Ransomes & Rapier W 80 walking dragline in No. 3 quarry.

This takes us up to the formation of Stewarts & Lloyds Minerals Ltd in 1950 and it is interesting to note that the 66 years of Market Overton's existence consisted of 22 years each under James Pain, Stanton and Stewarts & Lloyds Minerals/British Steel Corporation. In the first two periods operating methods and equipment had not altered fundamentally,

Market Overton Quarries. No. 2 quarry with Berry shovel in foreground. 20-ton Ruston shovel (RP 423) with long jib behind; and Ruston transporter. c 1935.

(B S C)

Market Overton Quarries. Calcine clamps east of the yard. May 1952.   (BSC)

but did so in many ways afterwards. The only quarry working in 1950 was No. 3; in 1951 No. 5 quarry was opened, south of the Thistleton road, about three quarters of a mile east of the bridge thereunder and reached by a branch tramway leaving the old line immediately south of the bridge. Calcine banks to deal with the output from No. 5 were put down in 1952 at

Market Overton Quarries. In the post World War II years it became increasingly common to place the rail tracks on the lip of the quarry, as shown here with a row of hoppers at No. 3 quarry on 26th May 1943. Dragline is a W 80 (R&R 976).   (BSC)

Market Overton Quarries. No. 3 quarry, showing the succession of working. R&R 5361 stripping shovel removes the overburden of Lincolnshire Limestone, and R&R 480 shovel loads ironstone into hopper wagons. Note the face ladder at right.   (B S C)

the northern end of the yard. The increased output and the calcining operations called for an increased locomotive stock, which went up to five in 1953, in which year also a scheme of improvement of the facilities was introduced, including the provision of new offices, locomotive shed and workshops, and the concreting of the rough bridleway to the main road. The old locomotive shed was built of red brick (made at Pain's Corby brickworks and so stamped) and later had a corrugated iron extension tacked on, when it was capable of holding four locomotives on its single road. The new shed, usually referred to as 'Cooper's shed' from the name of the then manager, had two widely-spaced roads beneath a pillarless roof of prestressed concrete coated with smoke-resistant paint. A well-equipped workshop lay behind.The new shed was brought into use in May 1955 and the track to the old shed was taken up a year or so later and the building used as a store. In 1953 also was started the experiment of laying the rail track on the lip of the quarry instead of on the quarry floor, which was tried in No. 3 quarry; later, the line was laid on the ironstone bed **in** the quarry. This quarry was closed in 1956 because of deterioration in the quality of the stone, and in the same year No. 6 quarry was opened up, about half a mile

Market Overton Quarries. W 90 Diesel Walking Dragline removing overburden at No. 5
quarry, 29th September 1954, shortly after opening.   (B S C)

due east of the administrative area, and stretching as far as Foss Lane
(Thistleton-Sewstern). No. 5 quarry was on ground leased from the
Ecclesiastical Commissioners and No. 6 also, plus land in Thistleton parish
of which Stewarts & Lloyds held the freehold. Both quarries were worked
northwards anti-clockwise.

Market Overton Quarries. No. 5 quarry, with 54RB dragline loading skips with ore for
calcining. April 1953.   (B S C)

Market Overton Quarries. No. 6 quarry, October 1958. 5361 stripping shovel removing rock at right, 110RB loading ironstone from below rail level. *JUNO* is just pulling away with a full load.

(B S C)

The expansion period up to 1957 was marked by the acquisition of more than a dozen machines, diesel and electric, some of them only temporarily for special jobs, but most of them larger machines than hitherto, to deal with the deeper quarrying as working moved east. No. 5 quarry was operated by diesel machines, Nos. 3 and 6 mainly by electrics. The smaller machines moved about on special jobs, e.g. a 43RB diesel dragline did the baring at No. 5 in 1952, then moved to No. 6 to strip overburden; but the larger machines tended to 'stay put'. There was a W 80 diesel walking dragline in No. 3, later replaced by a W90, with a 480 shovel for loading. At No. 5, a W 90 walking dragline removed overburden, and a 54RB dragline did the loading. Generally speaking, the working conditions at Market Overton became harder than at Buckminster, as the overburden reached greater proportions. The very deep No. 6 quarry required more massive machinery, and a 5361 Stripping Shovel was moved here from Deene pit, Corby, with a 100RB dragline for loading, replaced by a 110RB shovel in 1957; the latter was the only example in the Midlands ironstone field, and was immediately identifiable by the small cab at the side. Various machines were used in the quarrying industry for jobs only indirectly concerned with output, and for interest we list the battery of these used at No. 6 quarry, as recorded in the archives:-

431 shovel for diverting the stream; 100RB and W80 draglines for excavating the gullet: 54RB dragline for excavating the incline down to the ironstone: 5361 for excavating the corridor to stone and gullet.

Output in the later years went to Stanton, Corby and Irlam steelworks mostly, some to Scunthorpe, and also Holwell up to 1962. Demand for ironstone fell off in the middle 1960s; No. 5 quarry was closed in 1962 and calcining had ceased shortly before this, the site of the banks being restored in 1961/2. The line south from the loco. shed area then fell into disuse and the portion beyond Thistleton Road was lifted in 1962/3, and nearer to the shed area in 1964. The locomotive stock was reduced to two in 1963, working turn and turn about; in 1965, when trade picked up, both of them worked, one in the quarry and one the connecting line to Pains Sidings. In these last years the work was harder simply because of the greater depth of the quarry, hence more powerful locomotives were needed. By this time, output was required only for Scunthorpe, as Stanton Ironworks was supplied from Harlaxton and Woolsthorpe. This slump in demand culminated in cessation of quarrying at Market Overton in September 1966, when the Scunthorpe demand was met from Buckminster. Some trial loads went from Market Overton direct to Scunthorpe via Pains Sidings and Buckminster Sidings at this time,

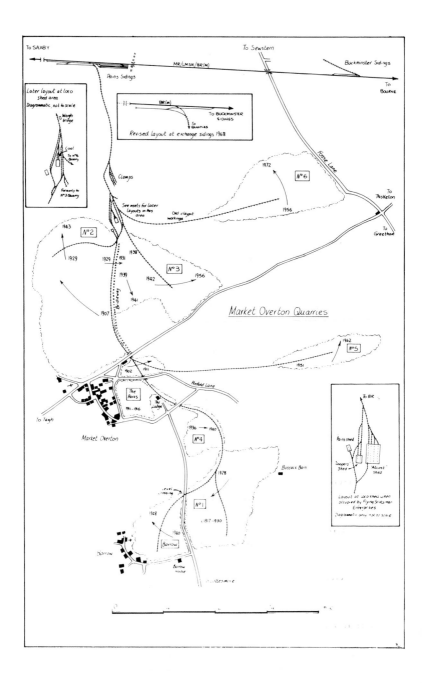

however, hauled throughout by a Buckminster locomotive. The two locomotives left were stored in the shed until the Scunthorpe requirement should pick up. Negotiations with British Railways to take Market Overton ore via Stainby had started as long ago as 1964 and on 2nd October 1967 diesel locomotive *FRANK* arrived from Oxfordshire Ironstone Co Ltd and commenced work the same day. From the railway point of view, Market Overton then became merely a subshed of the Buckminster system. The manager at Market Overton at the time of the 1950's expansion was Mr. Cooper, who was succeeded in December 1957 by Mr Sibley; when the quarries were combined with Buckminster, Mr. Sibley took charge of both and in November 1967 was succeeded by Mr. Burgess.

We will now describe the layout as it was in later years. At Pains Sidings there was the usual accommodation for full and empty wagons, and the quarry tramway turned southwards on a very tight curve, then followed the contours of the ground to the central area; its course was somewhat sinuous and climbed gently most of the way, with neat lineside hedges each side for the first half mile, an unusual feature for a mineral line. A public footpath crossed the route at one point, but walkers found it more convenient to follow the line of railway, hence the path to the east disappeared. The path is an extension of the bridleway from the Thistleton road. The ground at the office area was attractively situated, with an air of spaciousness, and always looked green and pleasant. The modern buildings erected in 1954/5 were neat and clean without imposing on the rusticity, while tucked away at the side was Pain's old locomotive shed of mellowed Corby brick.

The line southwards from the shed area was laid at the outset of operations and ran parallel to the bridleway, starting off level but descending in a cutting a short distance beyond the bridge. In the course of time this section of route became overgrown but more open conditions prevailed further south and east. The track was formerly all spiked to wooden sleepers on earth ballast, but in later years chaired track and concrete sleepers were used when relaying was necessary, and extended to most of the main line and yard area. Warning notices were put up where the vehicle route crossed the line, e.g. 'Beware oncoming trains' and 'Lane crossing ahead; loco whistle and proceed with caution' — both in black letters on a yellow board.

The first locomotives were four-wheelers but increasing haulage distances and heavier loads soon brought in six-wheelers as the preferred type. James Pain bought most of his locomotives new from Pecketts, and moved his locos around his quarries as traffic demanded. *LANCE* and

GORDON were named after two of his sons, and the origin of the names *IRONSTONE* and *OVERTON* is obvious; so too is *DARLINGTON*, which came from that town. She arrived in 1915, doubtless to tackle heavier wartime requirements, as did *ADDERLEY.* This last name is that of a quarry at Uppingham, where the loco. later worked for many years; it is not clear from Avonside records whether she was named *ADDERLEY* when new, but the plates she bore in later years were of Hunslet design, so were presumably a replacement pair, after Hunslet had acquired the goodwill of Avonside when the latter firm closed down. If the engine was destined for Uppingham in 1915, the name is understandable, even though the locomotive was temporarily diverted to Market Overton; if the loco. was ordered for Market Overton, then perhaps the name was not carried until she was moved to Uppingham quarries.

It will be noted that there were two locomotives named *UPPINGHAM*, both from Pain's quarries there. It seems logical to suppose that the later one (Avonside) displaced the smaller Peckett at Uppingham; if so, this would make the transfer of the latter to Market Overton about 1918, though the date is not recorded. Incidentally, this little Peckett was the sole

Market Overton Quarries. Avonside locomotive *ADDERLEY* — so named after the quarry at Uppingham where she originally worked — on 26th August 1962.

(Harold D. Bowtell)

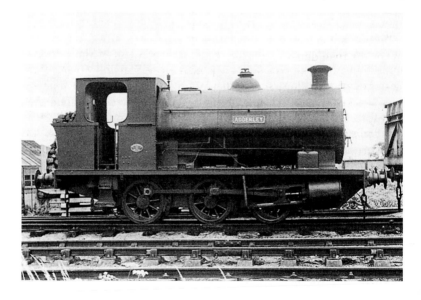

Market Overton Quarries. *HOLWELL No. 7*, a veteran Manning Wardle, in the yard on 1st July 1952. "A blistering hot day" Ken Cooper remarked—the tarpaulin was for shade, not shelter! (K. Cooper/IRS Collection)

survivor of Pain's old stock; she was used at Wirksworth quarries in Derbyshire in the early 1970s and was acquired by the Midland Railway Project for preservation in 1974, and later returned to Market Overton.

When Stanton took over, there were more than enough locomotives to cover the then diminished demand, as the Uppingham ones had been moved here following the closure of Uppingham quarries in 1926. Apart from *UPPINGHAM* herself, the whole lot were dispersed to other Stanton properties and replaced in turn by four locomotives from other quarries, but only one—*HOLWELL No. 7*—remained for more than a few months. She and *UPPINGHAM* were the mainstay of the motive power in the 1930s, but in 1938 there came from the Port of London Authority, *JASON*, an unusual machine for the quarries. She had a short wheelbase, and remained throughout the intensive working of the war years, helped by a second Manning Wardle from Middlesbrough.

This rather mixed bag was gradually disposed of when Stewarts & Lloyds Minerals took over, and larger and more modern locomotives appeared, to deal with the harder conditions obtaining. *RUTLAND*, a standard Barclay 15in. locomotive, was the first new locomotive for 39 years, but she was not quite up to the then heavier work consequent on the steep bank out of

135

Market Overton Quarries. The most unusual locomotive here was *JASON*, a Robert Stephenson engine from Port of London Authority. 1st July 1952.

(K. Cooper/IRS Collection)

No. 6 quarry, and was replaced by another new engine in 1958, the 'Austerity' *JUNO*, one of the last steamers to be supplied to the ironstone industry. *JUNO* was regarded as 'the best loco we have ever had' and *JUPITER* from Corby completed the steam scene at Market Overton; some Barclays were later borrowed from Buckminster for short periods but only as spare to the diesels, and *BUCKMINSTER* was not used at all. *JUPITER* had a steel firebox, which gave a bit of trouble with the hard Market Overton water. The use of classical names beginning with J, following *JASON*, will be noted; the origin of *RUTLAND* requires no explanation. Stewarts & Lloyds Minerals Ltd accepted diesels rather tardily, but Market Overton had one of the first; built by E. E. Baguley Ltd and supplied through Drewry Car Co Ltd, she went to Harlaxton first but then moved to Market Overton, and had a 387hp Cummins engine. Ostensibly on trials, she did no work here because of the recession in demand, and was eventually sent back to Harlaxton; but for the arrival of the Oxfordshire Ironstone Sentinels she may well have been the forerunner of a fleet of Baguley diesels in the quarries.

The steam locomotives were all painted green, as far as is known, but differed in detail. Of the Pecketts that came new, *IRONSTONE* is known to

Market Overton Quarries. One of the last two steam locomotives for the ironstone industry was this 'Austerity' Hunslet, *JUNO*, supplied in 1958. A 'stock shot' by Ken Cooper — engine in good condition, good background, rods down. 23rd May 1961. (K. Cooper/IRS Collection)

Market Overton Quarries. *JUPITER*, one of the Corby fleet of 56 class locomotives, drafted to Market Overton in 1962, and where she was given the name.   (RRM Archives)

have borne the maker's standard livery of green lined black edged yellow, with brass nameplates, and *LANCE*, *GORDON*, and *OVERTON* were probably the same. The commonest livery was dark green lined black edged white and appeared on both *UPPINGHAM*s, *HOLWELL No. 7*, *JASON*, *JUBILEE*, *STAINBY*, *SEWSTERN*, *BUCKMINSTER*, and *RUTLAND*. Some were in plain dark green — *DARLINGTON*, *CURZON*, *BUCCLEUCH, No. 9, HOLWELL No. 16*, the last having red rods. *51* was mid green with black 'handleable' parts, and brass numberplate; *60* similar, with *S & L MINERALS LTD* in white on the cab and later with *JUPITER* painted in yellow on the tank. *JUNO* was plain green with red rods, and with the plant number painted on (see under Buckminster). The diesels showed a departure from the traditional green. The Drewry was dark blue with red rods and with *DREWRY* at the front and rear. *FRANK* and *MAUD* were maroon lined black edged yellow. When quarrying was resumed in 1967, the two ex-Oxfordshire Ironstone Sentinels did most of the work and they looked smart with their livery sparkling in the sun. When the

Market Overton Quarries. The first railtour with *JUNO* hauling the train towards Pains Sidings, 3rd October 1964.

(H. A. Gamble)

locomotive shed was used by diesels only, the 'pots' were covered over, except for two on the east side, with the covers lifted on bricks.

From October 2nd 1967 all output from Market Overton was sent out via the BR line between Pains Sidings and Buckminster Sidings to Stainby and High Dyke, destined for Redbourn steelworks in Scunthorpe. Market Overton office was closed, as the administration was carried out by Buckminster, but two locomotives were retained, one to work the quarry and the other to take the output to Stainby. There was little change in the quarries, though operations in the deep No. 6 quarry were always impressive and attracted enthusiast attention; but there was a lot of experimenting on the locomotive side as this was integrated into the Buckminster system, and is described in that section. In the final phase an ex BR class 14 worked from Buckminster to collect Market Overton's output, but a Sentinel diesel was retained to work the quarry.

With the continuing contraction of the industry, the end came on 31st December 1971, on which day *FRANK* was sent to Buckminster yard.

Flying Scotsman Enterprises. The arrival of *PENDENNIS CASTLE* at Pains Sidings, 23rd June 1972. (Mrs France)

The preservation schemes

The facilities for locomotives at Market Overton were unusually good, and as long ago as 1965 the Birmingham Locomotive Club Industrial Locomotive Information Section (later the Industrial Railway Society) had suggested that they would be ideal for locomotive preservation; and when the locomotive shed and other buildings were auctioned by Shouler & Son of Melton Mowbray on 2nd May 1972 they were purchased by the Hon. John Gretton on behalf of Flying Scotsman Enterprises, primarily as a winter base for main line express locomotives so that restoration work could be carried out on them. The first arrival, Mr. Gretton's Baguley diesel in bright blue livery, came in the third week of June 1972 and helped to prepare the site for the reception of locomotives and rolling stock from Didcot. The famous GWR locomotive *PENDENNIS CASTLE* was jointly owned by John Gretton and W. H. McAlpine and on 23rd June she was towed from Didcot by a BR diesel, but in light steam, and was handed over to the BSC diesel at Stainby Sidings. Some BR men from Grantham were required for pilot duty and among those who volunteered was at least one who remembered her visit to the area in the 1925 locomotive exchanges. The *'Castle'* was accompanied by a coach and an observation car. No difficulty was experienced in negotiating the Buckminster line and progress was recorded by a number of cameras; the curve from Pains Sidings towards Market Overton was a bit too sharp however and the engine was left on BR metals for the weekend until the curve was eased. Market Overton shed had been given a spring clean (though it had always been in good condition) and the stock was put under cover.

Extensive modifications to the track layout were made in 1973 for the storage and movement of newly acquired locomotives and rolling stock. The lines to the west and east of the shed were united at the south end, with an extension running a short distance along the course of the former line to the southern quarries; a spur was put in off the western line and track run into the old Pain's loco. shed, which was restored to its former purpose of housing industrial locomotives, and was provided with new doors; and a huge eight-road shed of prestressed concrete was erected in the yard to the east. This last was built by 'Atcost' and as a pioneer of its kind was formally opened in August 1973. Locomotives and rolling stock from various sources continued to arrive, some direct from industry and some from other preservation sites, and by the end of 1973 there were eleven locomotives of various kinds, including the express locomotives *PENDENNIS CASTLE* and *FLYING SCOTSMAN*; and, at the other end of

Flying Scotsman Enterprises. Market Overton yard in preservation days, showing the three locomotive sheds. Pain's (far left, to right of telephone pole), Coopers (centre) and Atcost (right). *PENDENNIS CASTLE* and D 2381 in background. c June 1972. (B S C)

the scale, a narrow gauge Peckett from South Africa.

While these events were taking place at Market Overton, Buckminster Quarries were being considered for development as a Leisure Centre, with trips over the former ironstone railway hauled by a quarry locomotive as a major attraction; these activities were coordinated by Buckminster Enterprises, a subsidiary of Buckminster Trust Estate, the landowners. While these two preservation schemes were entirely different in concept, they were forced to work together by the fact that in the final years of quarrying both systems had operated as one unit; and this they did, in a spirit of friendly cooperation. From then on, they stood or fell together. One example was provided by the rebuilding of 'Merchant Navy' 35029 *ELLERMAN LINES*; this locomotive had been purchased from Woodham Bros' scrapyard in Barry for the National Railway Museum at York, with the aim of making a 'sectioned' locomotive, i.e. one with various parts cut away to reveal the internal mechanism, so that observers could see how a steam locomotive was built. This task had been assigned to Flying

Flying Scotsman Enterprises. 35029 awaiting restoration in Market Overton shops. 1974. (RRM Archives)

143

Scotsman Enterprises, but they subcontracted the job to Buckminster Enterprises, who had very good engineering facilities.

For the first eight months of 1974 both sides continued with their plans. At Market Overton further engines were acquired, while *FLYING SCOTSMAN* departed 16th April 1974 for a programme of special workings in the summer months; and there was a fair usage of the connection to High Dyke via Buckminster to bring in materials such as ballast and for stock movement. However, BR wished to close the High Dyke line, and since Market Overton was regarded by FSE primarily as a home base for their express locomotives, a connection to BR was essential, and it was therefore planned to reinstate the four-mile connection between Pains Sidings and Saxby. Rail and sleepers were acquired from a variety of local sources—the former BR Cottesmore branch, sidings at Stainby, and the quarry railway at Harlaxton (closed in February 1974); all this material was stacked in Market Overton yard and some taken to Pains Sidings, where a start on the new connecting link was made in July. This venture was undertaken jointly by Flying Scotsman Enterprises and Buckminster Enterprises, both of whom considered the link with BR to be vital. It was also hoped that when the line was complete BR trains would be allowed to run through to Pains Sidings.

Alas! for their high hopes; because of the uncertain economic climate of the times, both parties decided to abandon their schemes, individually and collectively. Of the proposed connection to Saxby seven lengths of rail and sleepers were laid in July 1974, and that was all; they were never even ballasted. BR announced that the connection to High Dyke would be severed on 6th October 1974 and the first week on October was one of feverish activity as coaching stock was taken out via High Dyke, followed at 7.35am on Saturday 5th October by *PENDENNIS CASTLE* en route to Neville Hill shed to join up with *FLYING SCOTSMAN* for transfer to Carnforth.

What may be termed the final Buckminster Railway consisted of three components—the Buckminster quarry system, the Market Overton quarry system, and the intervening section of BR line—that had been fused into one railway controlled by Stewarts & Lloyds Minerals Ltd; but when dismantlement came, the tangled historical skein was unravelled in a few weeks, and the three sections treated as separate entities once more.

The Buckminster portion was summarily dealt with; the track was sold to John Lee & Son (Grantham) Ltd, who commenced lifting operations at the northern end in December 1974, and the buildings at the yard were leased as units of a small trading estate, with a deadline of 6th January 1975 set for

Flying Scotsman Enterprises. When the twin preservation schemes at Market Overton and Buckminster were at their most active, it was proposed to relay the connection from Pains Sidings to Saxby Junction to replace the closed High Dyke connection to BR. The photograph shows the new track towards Saxby on 12th November 1974.   (Eric Tonks)

evacuation by Buckminster Enterprises. Two of the locomotives came to Market Overton; AB 1931, belonging to Peter Layfield, arrived on New Year's Day and was put, appropriately enough, in Pain's old shed, while 35029 moved into the Cooper shed on Saturday, January 4th. Most of the heavy work of sectioning had been done but there were small details to be completed, and the locomotive then painted for York Museum. This event attracted public attention, but the movement of AB 1931, hardly noticed at the time, proved to have greater historical significance.

The rundown at Market Overton was a much lengthier procedure. D 2381 was engaged with the Crewe 'cab' in collecting material acquired for the Saxby line from Buckminster yard and from Pains Sidings, and about January 1975 the illfated lengths of track that had been laid were taken up, just ahead of T. W. Ward's gang lifting the BR section. The rest of the Market Overton line was left in situ, with the gate across the line locked (in working days it was normally left open). A few special trips were run for enthusiasts, the last occasion being on 7th September 1975, the day of the handing-over ceremony of 35029 to representatives of York Museum.

JOHN and *GLENFIELD* worked this train, and they drew 35029 out of the Atcost shed. She looked magnificent; Buckminster had made a fine job of the sectioning and Market Overton had done the painting superbly. There were a few very short speeches, mainly in light-hearted vein, and among the invited audience were the teams responsible for the work at both quarry workshops; to them the occasion was more of a sad one, representing as it did the last constructive railway activity at these shops.

35029 departed for York by road during the following week. By then a Mr. R. Duce of Wymeswold had an option of the Market Overton site for the restoration and sale of vintage cars, and further contraction of railway facilities was put in hand. There had been desultory efforts to dispose of the site still as a railway preservation centre, but these had come to nothing. In October and November the line from Pains Sidings to the top of the yard was lifted, as required by the terms negotiated with the British Steel

Flying Scotsman Enterprises. 'Merchant Navy' 35029 was rebuilt in Buckminster shops as a sectioned exhibit for the National Railway Museum at York, and was then painted at Market Overton. She was handed over officially to the NRM on this day, 7th September 1975. (Eric Tonks)

Corporation, and in November all track in the Atcost shed and the yard north of it was taken up. The remaining locomotive stock was all housed in the Cooper shed except for Peter Layfield's Barclay in Pain's shed, and the narrow gauge Peckett dumped in the yard, awaiting collection by the Welsh Highland Railway group.

Even at this time, items of interest continued to turn up. An ex-Army Austin 'Champ' vehicle, with its road wheels removed and replaced by flanged wheels, arrived from Mr. McAlpine's preservation site at Fawley, Buckinghamshire, in November. Possibly it was thought to be of use in track-lifting work. For the same purpose also two flat wagons were acquired from the BR Cottesmore branch terminus, where they had gravitated when the Exton Park quarry system was being dismantled; they were still in their original grey livery with *United Steel Companies Ore Mining Branch Exton Park No. 1* and ditto *No. 2* in white letters. They were purchased early in 1974. A discovery in the workshops was a nameplate *COUNTY OF RUTLAND* made of wood with cork lettering, and a perfect replica of a GWR 'County' class plate. It had been intended to cast nameplates to this design for the Bagnall saddle tank locomotive.

Negotiations with Mr Duce were finalised with the transfer of ownership of the site to him on 20th March 1976, and Flying Scotsman Enterprises were required to remove their property by that date; D 2381 only just made it, departing the previous day! The departure of her for Carnforth and the lifting of all the track in the yard and sheds imparted the desolate appearance common to such situations; but all was not quite lost. Peter Layfield still had his Andrew Barclay locomotive, partly dismantled in the Pain's shed, and two friends Richard Knight and Terry Robinson had each bought a locomotive (respectively P 2110 and AE 1973) from FSE. Mr. Duce generously gave permission for a small group to remain on the site and to lay track along the old cutting to the south pits; but this did not extend to the use of Pain's shed, as he required this, or at any rate the ground on which it stood. Mr. Duce altered the yard to suit his requirements; the pits in the Cooper shed were filled in and concreted, and the floor of the Atcost shed was levelled, well before he moved in in the spring of 1976. Pain's locomotive shed, sadly, was dismantled at the end of January 1978 to make way for another building.

The three partners formed the Market Overton Industrial Railway Association and lost no time in laying track from the south end of the yard along the cutting as far as a pile of rough limestone that had been deposited by the side of the bridleway and which had spilled over into the cutting. None of the locomotives disposed on the track were in working order at the time, with tarpaulins for their protection, but it was hoped to instal a typical ironstone quarry shed on a run-round loop. The lack of cover hardly mattered in the torrid summer of 1976 (though it was a bit too hot for heavy work) but winter would be different. The ironstone system at Harston (Woolsthorpe) was closed in 1974, leaving the shed standing in isolation near the road. The building had been purchased by Mr. F. G. Cann of Finedon, but he resold it to the Association, who dismantled it in November 1976 for re-erection at Market Overton. Planning permission to put up the shed was received in April 1977, Mr. Duce having raised no objection.

The Association slowly but steadily grew in numbers, and were not lacking in initiative or energy. The track was put in better shape, an inspection pit was dug, and it was hoped eventually to extend the track as far as Thistleton Road, nearly three quarters of a mile in total. Locomotives were the principal interest, and the members managed to remove tanks for boiler inspection, no mean feat without any lifting tackle; and the restoration of a Hudswell Clarke saddle tank from Fawley was undertaken, under the supervision of Mr. Devitt, who had remained here when FSE pulled out. AE 1973 was put in steam in August 1977 and given nameplates *DORA*. A number of wagons were also obtained, an important aspect of industrial railway preservation; the first was a wooden three-plank wagon of Cambrian Railways origin, from the Beeston Boiler Co of Nottingham. It was hoped to paint this in the livery of a James Pain wagon, but information on this point was not discoverable — even Gordon Pain did not know it! The Association also hoped to establish a museum to display relics and photographs appertaining to the ironstone industry.

There was however a considerable doubt overshadowing the whole enterprise; since *MOIRA* paid no rent, they had no security of tenure, and remained on the site solely at the discretion of the owner. Efforts to find an alternative site were made, with ironstone associations as an integral part of their plans, and these were redoubled when at last, on 26th August 1978, a letter was received from Roland Duce Ltd, giving the Association one year in which to vacate the site. One of Mr. Duce's objections was the 'scrapyard' appearance that potential customers of his received as they came down the approach road. An array of cabs and tanks is inseparable from locomotive preservation, but it must be remembered that matters had changed quite a lot since the original permission had been given. At that time there were three locomotives owned by three partners; by the middle of 1978 this had swelled to eight locomotives, ten wagons and a group of ten to twenty weekend volunteers, with every prospect of further

Market Overton Industrial Railway Association. *DORA* (AE 1973) takes a group of enthusiasts along the relaid section of the route to Nos. 4 and 5 quarries. On the left is the site of No. 2 quarry, and on the right the embankment up to the bridleway to the yard. April 1978.

(RRM Archives/Ian Wilson)

enlargement under the energetic leadership of Gordon Kobish. Mr. Duce probably considered that things were getting out of hand, notwithstanding the improved appearance of several of the locomotives.

Thus the second attempt at railway preservation at the Market Overton site faded out, for reasons entirely different from those attending the demise of the Buckminster Enterprises/Flying Scotsman Enterprises schemes, and one can only speculate whether, in other circumstances, a successful outcome would have been possible. The bi-polar Buckminster-Market Overton system was rather too unwieldy for lasting comfort, and while for the two years from mid-1972 to mid-1974 they worked in complete harmony the aims of the two owners were very different. A more limited preservation effort, involving only the use of industrial locomotives, might have had a greater chance of success and certainly would have been a more fitting memorial. The express locomotives, the director's saloons and the main line trappings, brought a glamour to the system, but they were very obviously out of place; we need shed no tears at their removal to more suitable surroundings.

After considering various possible alternatives, the Association decided to move to the end of the former BR Cottesmore branch — not a quarry but with strong associations with the ironstone industry — and moved thither the locomotives and rolling stock in December 1979. Market Overton then became just another abandoned quarry site, but retaining traces of its more recent occupation.

Physical Remains

As with Buckminster, the course of the 'main line' from Pains Sidings to the administrative area is traceable throughout, mainly alongside hedges; and while the small ancillary hedges were taken out about 1980, the crops still did not extend much over the sterile trackbed. The switchback character of the line is very obvious, and about half a mile from the junction there is a weighbridge hut, somewhat vandalised. The buildings grouped round the yard date from various phases of activity. The original Pain's locomotive shed right by the hedge on the west side of the yard was demolished in 1978 and only the concrete floor remains. In the middle of the yard are the buildings constructed in the 1950s, including office, workshops and locomotive shed (the 'Cooper' shed) complete with rails, while at the east lies the huge 'Atcost' building erected by Flying Scotsman Enterprises. Further buildings were put up as part of the 'Roland Duce Industrial Estate'.

To the west of the shed area were two curved gullets from No. 2 quarry, filled with water and leased to fishing interests; these two artificial lakes were not at the same level, which struck the eye oddly. No. 2 Quarry stretched from the lower lake south to Thistleton Road, and east towards the escarpment; as usual the ground was at a lower level, rather hummocky in parts and crossed by replacement hedges. The northern part of this area was smoothed over in 1983, the lower lake filled in and the northern part of the main line cutting filled in to the same level; the rest may follow suit, obviously, but was intact in 1984. The 'sausage' water tank (formerly a Lancashire boiler?) lay on the ground then.

The main line that once served the quarries east and south of Market Overton village ran alongside the bridleway that gives public access to the yard, and its course is still visible on the western side; starting off from the shed area level with the bridleway, it soon descended behind the hedge into a bushy cutting—but the top section has now been levelled, as mentioned above. Reference to the survey maps shows that the ironstone under the bridleway was removed as part of No. 3 quarry; this may not be immediately apparent, as the route is irregular. If one approaches from the direction of Market Overton, the right hand hedge is obviously an old one containing mature trees (though reduced in 1977/8 by Dutch Elm disease) but as one turns the first bend, the bridleway goes down a short dip and the trees cease abruptly, leaving an almost pure hawthorn hedge—clearly a replacement of that at original ground level. The bridleway itself was remetalled about 1980, as far as the industrial estate, and new trees were then planted alongside. On the left, hedges were being removed in the 1980s and the old tramway cutting being filled in.

The bridge under Thistleton Road has been filled in and the parapets replaced by fences; but the cutting on the south side remained, well hemmed in by trees, and waterlogged in parts, until the summer of 1978, when the fence was removed and a rough access road made down to a new pavilion on the sunken ground used as a sports field. The branch to No. 5 quarry turned eastwards off this section and the course of the line is just about traceable (where not ploughed up) to the terminal gullet, which is unrestored and descending from 20 to 40 feet deep. The face, showing ironstone and limestone, is now overgrown by goat willow, and carrying some water. Immediately north of Pinfold Lane there is on the east side a further arc of water at the terminating face of the old quarry, this water being stocked with fish and leased to the South Witham Angling Club. To the west of the lane, behind the cottages, are the grounds of the Market Overton Cricket Club in an old quarry, the final working face of which is still quite clear. It is to be hoped that these sporting fraternities will help to preserve a little bit of the quarrying sites.

The track ran beneath Pinfold Lane by a bridge that has been filled in, but the footings of the parapets are to be seen in the grass verge — evidently the bridge parapets were much closer than the hedges here. Ground on the south side of Pinfold Lane has also been excavated (as shown by its low level) and by Bowling Green Lane was being built upon 1975-78; the route crossed under the next lane ('Back Lane') by a bridge, also now gone, and beyond there was a cutting with high banks on each side, the latter overgrown with trees, but these were cut down in 1975 and the cutting filled in. The route then peters out in more open country in the flattish area of No. 4 quarry and No. 1 quarry extension; in the vicinity of the airfield is a pool on ground from which the ore has been extracted (Bussack Barn pit). Quarrying extended up to the Cottesmore road and beyond it to Barrow pit, but the site of the crossing has left no visible traces at all; lower ground on each side and the pure hawthorn hedges provide the evidence of quarrying. The road here commands a fine view of the Vale of Catmose; a bit windswept for this reason, which probably accounts for the fact that the fifty or so Lombardy Poplars once here were reduced by 1977 to five, and by the summer of 1978 this remnant had gone.

Two other quarries remain to be mentioned; No. 3, which has left a water-filled gullet towards the Thistleton road, and the last quarry, No. 6, still a very deep gullet running up to the road from Thistleton to Sewstern (Foss Lane). This remains as an excellent and most impressive example — like a small Grand Canyon — of a modern deep ironstone quarry, showing clearly the successive strata, including Lincolnshire Limestone and as the base, the ten feet or so of deep red-brown ironstone. Old hedges on the surface have been replaced by hawthorn hedges flanked each side by wire, very difficult to scale.

Grid References

887188	Pains Siding (MR junction)
889176	Locomotive shed
889173	Water tank by bridleway
890517	Bridge under Thistleton road
892165	Bridge under Pinfold Lane
894163	Bridge under 'back lane'
895156	Level crossing to Barrow Pit
891152	Barrow Quarry terminus
899173	No. 3 Quarry terminus
910170	No. 5 Quarry terminus
905180	No. 6 Quarry terminus
883189	New track for Flying Scotsman Enterprises

Locomotives

Gauge; 4ft.8½in.

No.	Name	Type	Cyl	Mkr	No.	Year	Cylinders	Diam.	Notes	Ref
	LANCE	0-4-0ST	OC	P	1038	1906	12 x 18in.	3ft.0½in.	New 7/1906	(1)
	IRONSTONE	0-4-0ST	OC	P	1050	1907	12 x 18in.	3ft.0½in.	New 2/1907	(2)
	OVERTON	0-6-0ST	IC	P	1218	1910	16 x 22in.	3ft.10in.	New 1/1910	(3)
	GORDON	0-4-0ST	OC	P	819	1900	10 x 14in.	2ft.6½in.	(a)	(4)
	DARLINGTON	0-6-0ST	IC	HE	421	1887	14 x 18in.	3ft.1in.	(b)	(5)
		Reb J. F. Wake				1915				
	ADDERLEY	0-6-0ST	OC	AE	1694	1915	14½ x 20in.	3ft.3in.	New 1915	(6)
	UPPINGHAM	0-4-0ST	OC	P	1257	1912	12 x 18in.	3ft.0½in.	(c)	(7)
	UPPINGHAM	0-6-0ST	OC	AE	1806	1918	14½ x 20in.	3ft.3in.	(d)	(8)
	BUCCLEUCH	0-6-0ST	OC	P	1232	1910	14 x 20in.	3ft.7in.	(e)	(9)
	CURZON	0-6-0ST	IC	HE	422	1887	14 x 18in.	3ft.1in.	(f)	(10)
		Reb Holwell				1931				
	HOLWELL No.7	0-6-0ST	IC	MW	556	1875	12 x 17in.	3ft. 0in.	(g)	(11)
No. 9		0-4-0ST	OC	HC	1285	1917	13 x 18in.	3ft.1in.	(h)	(12)
	JASON	0-6-0ST	OC	RS	3170	1905	16 x 20in.	3ft.6in.	(i)	(13)
	JUBILEE	0-6-0ST	IC	MW	1641	1904	13 x 18in.	3ft.1 7/16in.	(j)	(14)
	HOLWELL No. 16	0-4-0ST	OC	HL	3304	1917	14 x 22in.	3ft.6in.	(k) Scr 12/1961	
51		0-6-0ST	IC	RS	7003	1940	16 x 22in.	3ft.6in.	(l)	(15)
	RUTLAND	0-6-0ST	OC	AB	2351	1954	15 x 22in.	3ft.5in.	New 1/1954	(16)
	JUNO	0-6-0ST	IC	HE	3850	1958	18 x 26in.	4ft.0½in.	(m)	(17)
60	JUPITER	0-6-0ST	IC	RSH	7667	1950	18 x 26in.	4ft.0½in.	(n)	(18)
	STAINBY	0-6-0ST	OC	AB	2313	1951	15 x 22in.	3ft.5in.	(o)	(19)
	BUCKMINSTER	0-6-0ST	OC	AB	2050	1938	15 x 22in.	3ft.5in.	(p)	(20)
	SEWSTERN	0-6-0ST	OC	AB	2314	1951	15 x 22in.	3ft.5in.	(q)	(21)
	-	0-6-0DH		Bg	3601	1964	375hp		(r)	(22)
	FRANK	0-4-0DH		RR	10209	1965	311hp	40ton	(s)	(23)
	MAUD	0-4-0DH		S	10142	1962	311hp	30ton	(t)	(24)

(a) ex Glendon East Quarries 1912
(b) ex J. F. Wake, Darlington 11/1915 (Orig. T. A. Walker, Manchester Ship Canal)
(c) ex Uppingham Quarries, 1918 (?)
(d) ex Uppingham Quarries by 7/1923
(e) ex Glendon East Quarries 1/1930
(f) ex Buckminster Quarries 11/1931
(g) ex Holwell Works 1/1934 (prev. Buckminster Quarries)
(h) ex Eaton Quarries 10/1935
(i) formerly Port of London Authority, sent by them to RSH 6/1937, and reb. there 1938; acquired through George Cohen Sons & Co Ltd, Darlington 2/1938.
(j) ex Cochrane & Co Ltd, Middlesbrough 2/1941
(k) ex Cochrane & Co Ltd, Middlesbrough 3/1948
(l) ex Gretton Brook, Corby 8/1951 (Sysonby Lodge records give 7/1951)
(m) ex Buckminster Quarries 5/1958
(n) ex Corby Quarries 8/1962
(o) ex Buckmister Quarries 10/1967
(p) ex Buckminster Quarries 2/1968
(q) ex Buckminster Quarries 7/1968
(r) ex Harlaxton Quarries 3/1965
(s) ex Oxfordshire Ironstone Co Ltd 10/1967
(t) ex Oxfordshire Ironstone Co Ltd 2/1968

(1) to Thos. W. Ward Ltd, Charlton Works, Sheffield; to Whitecross Co Ltd, Warrington 1/1917
(2) to Glendon North Quarries 1928
(3) to Stanton Ironworks, 1930
(4) to Thos. W. Ward Ltd, Sheffield
(5) to Stanton Ironworks 1929; to Glendon East Quarries 7/1929
(6) to Uppingham Quarries c 1918; ex Uppingham c 1927; To Glendon East Quarries 7/1928: ex Eaton Quarries 3/1953. To Buckminster Quarries 3/1954; ex Buckminster 5/1955. Scr on site 12/1962. (in Sysonby Lodge records shown as 1/1963)
(7) to Holwell Works 6/1931; rebuilt; ex Holwell 1/1932. To Holwell Works 3/1947. To Bowne & Shaw, Wirksworth, Derbyshire 9/1947
(8) to Uppingham Quarries by 2/1924; ex Uppingham c 1927: to Buckminster Quarries 10/1930
(9) to Glendon East Quarries 11/1933
(10) to Eaton Quarries 12/1932
(11) to British Iron Management Ltd, Roanhead, Furness 1/1944; ex Roanhead 6/1944. To Holwell Works 7/1948: ex Holwell Works with new boiler 9/1949: to Eaton Quarries 2/1954
(12) to Glendon East Quarries 10/1936
(13) to Holwell Works 11/1949; rebuilt 1950: ex Holwell 5/1950: to Buckminster Quarries 1/1963
(14) to Cochrane & Co Ltd, 8/1948
(15) to Buckminster Quarries 4/1963
(16) to Woolsthorpe Quarries 5/1958
(17) to Buckminster Quarries 2/1968
(18) to Buckminster Quarries 10/1967
(19) to Buckminster Quarries 7/1968
(20) to Buckminster Quarries 2/1969

(21) to Buckminster Quarries 10/1969
(22) to Harlaxton Quarries 5/1966
(23) to Buckminster Quarries 10/1967; ex Buckminster 11/1968. To Buckminster 31/12/1971
(24) to Irchester Quarries 2/1969

Quarry Machines

Steam Machines

12 ton	S.Shovel	Wh	174	1906(?)	1½ Cu.Yds.	30ft.	New 1906(?)		(1)
No. 12	S.Shovel	RP	321	1910	2 Cu.Yds.	26ft.		(a)	(2)
No. 20	S.Shovel	RP	423	1914	2¼ Cu.Yds.	30ft.		(b)	(3)
15 ton	S.Shovel	Berry		1907	2 Cu.Yds.	30ft.		(c)	(4)
	S.Transporter	RP		1915				(d)	(5)
No. 8	S.Shovel	RP	346	1912	½ Cu.Yd.	25ft.		(e)	(6)
No. 2	Class 14 S.Stripping Shovel. Caterpillar	BU	877	c1918	1½ Cu.Yds.	77ft.		(f)	(7)
No. 10	S.Dragline	RH	788	1923	¾ Cu.Yd.	55ft.		(g)	(8)

(a) ex Edmund Nuttall, Contractor
(b) ex Uppingham Quarries 1926. Later with 26ft. jib
(c) ex ?, 1926
(d) ex Buckminster Quarries 9/1928
(e) ex Eaton Quarries 1/1936
(f) ex Buckminster Quarries 12/1937
(g) ex Buckminster Quarries 6/1941. Formerly Shovel

(1) At No. 2 Qy 1936. Scr 1940
(2) At No. 2 Qy 1936. Scr c 1941
(3) At No. 2 Qy 1936. Scr
(4) At No. 2 Qy; to No. 3 Qy. Scr 10/1938
(5) At No. 2 Qy; To No. 3 Qy by 1936. Scr 1941
(6) At No. 4 Qy (?). To Holwell Works 8/1937
(7) to Thos. W. Ward Ltd for scrap c 11/1950
(8) to Glendon Quarries 1/1942; ex Glendon 7/1946. To South Witham Quarries 12/1946

Diesel and Electric Machines

Model	Description	Maker	No.	Year	Capacity	Reach	New	Note	Ref
43RB	D.Dragline. Crawler	RB	3015	1936	¾ Cu.Yd.	60ft.	New 6/1936	(a)	(1)
W 80	D.Walking Dragline	R&R	976	1940	2½Cu.Yds.	80ft.	New 10/1940	(b)	(2)
21RB	D.Dragline. Crawler	RB						(c)	(3)
No. 4	PP.Dragline. Caterpillar	RH	1200	1927	⅜ Cu.Yd.	40ft.		(d)	(4)
21RB	D.Dragline	RB	2383	1933	⅜ Cu.Yd.	50ft.		(e)	(5)
55RB	E.Dragline. Crawler	RB	5666	1941		70ft.		(f)	(6)
55RB	E.Crane	RB	4975	1940	2 Cu.Yds.	60ft.		(g)	(7)
43RB	D.Dragline	RB	14076	1952	1½ Cu.Yds.	50ft.	New 2/1952		(8)
10RB	D.Clamshell digger. Crawler	RB	14897	1952	⅜ Cu.Yd.(?)	35ft.	New 4/1952		(9)
490	E.Shovel/Dragline	R&R	1191	1941	(2½ Cu.Yds. (-	28ft. 75ft.		(h)	(10)
5361	E.Stripping Shovel	R&R	284	1935	9 Cu.Yds.	116ft.		(i)	(11)
54RB	D. Dragline. Crawler	RB	15168	1953	2¾ Cu.Yds.	70ft	New 4/1953		(12)
W 90	D. Walking Dragline	R&R	2493	1953	(2½ Cu.Yds. (2 Cu.Yds.	102ft. 114ft.	New 1953	(j)	(13)
431	D. Dragline	R&R	451	1936				(k)	(14)
480	E. Dragline. Caterpillar	R&R	212	1934	2 Cu.Yds.	50ft.		(l)	(15)
100RB	E.Dragline. Caterpillar	RB	3682	1938	4 Cu.Yds.	60ft.		(m)	(16)
480 No.5	E.Shovel. Caterpillar	R&R	450	1936	3 Cu.Yds.	27ft.6in.		(n)	(17)
22RB	D.Dragline. Back-acter	RB	20121	1955	¾ Cu.Yd.	40ft.	New 12/1955		(18)
110RB	E.Shovel. High lift	RB	22160	1957	3½ Cu.Yds.	50ft.	New 7/1957		(19)
54RB	D.Dragline	RB	22355	1957				(o)	(20)
55RB	E.Shovel. High lift	RB	5665	1941	2½ Cu.Yds.	29ft.		(p)	(21)

(a) later 1½ Cu.Yds. 40ft.
(b) 2 Cu.Yds. 90ft. from 8/1953
(c) ex ?. (Could be RB 2383 — as below)
(d) ex Glendon Quarries 8/1946
(e) ex South Witham Quarries 8/1947
(f) ex Eaton Quarries 9/1951. Later converted to shovel — 1¾ Cu.Yds. 22ft.
(g) ex Buckminster Quarries 1/1952
(h) ex Buckminster Quarries 6/1952
(i) ex Corby Quarries (Deene) 1952
(j) later 2 Cu.Yds. 114ft.
(k) ex Woolsthorpe Quarries c 2/1955
(l) ex Buckminster Quarries 4/1955
(m) ex Buckminster Quarries 5/1955
(n) ex Buckminster Quarries c 1955
(o) ex Tilton Quarries c 1963
(p) ex Wellingborough Quarries 4/1968

(1) At No. 4 Qy. To Holwell Quarries 3/1944; ex Holwell 9/1944. To Buckminster Quarries 8/1947; ex Buckminster; to Woolsthorpe Quarries 1954
(2) At No. 3 Qy; No. 6 Qy by 1955. To Thistleton site 1/1957
(3) Opening Barrow face 1940. To ?
(4) to Nuthall sandpits, Nottinghamshire 3/1947. ex Nuthall 5/1951. Scr 1952
(5) to Buckminster Quarries 8/1948
(6) to Woolsthorpe Quarries 5/1955
(7) At No. 6 Qy 1955. To Wirksworth Quarries, Derbyshire 8/1954. ex Wirksworth 12/1955. To Buckminster Quarries 3/1956
(8) At No. 5 Qy; to No. 6 Qy by 1956. To Thistleton (?) 2/1958
(9) to Wirksworth Quarries 6/1954
(10) to Harlaxton Quarries 5/1957
(11) At No. 6 Qy. To ?, 1972
(12) At No. 5 Qy. To No. 6 Qy by 1955. To Harlaxton Quarries c 1967
(13) At No. 3 Qy; to No. 5 Qy. To Buckminster Quarries 1959
(14) Opening No. 6 Qy 1955. Scr c 1961
(15) At No. 3 Qy. To Buckminster Quarries 1956
(16) At No. 6 Qy. To Woolsthorpe Quarries 10/1958. ex Woolsthorpe. Scr 1/1974
(17) At No. 3 Qy. To No. 6 Qy. Scr 9/1971
(18) to Corby Quarries 3/1972
(19) At No. 6 Qy. To Corby Quarries (Oakley) 7/1963
(20) to Yorkshire & Lincolnshire Plant Hire, Scunthorpe, 4/1973
(21) At No. 6 Qy. Scr 12/1976

Locomotives acquired for preservation at Market Overton

(1). Flying Scotsman Enterprises

Gauge; 4ft. 8½in.

No. 5		0-4-0DM		Bg	3027	1939	(a)	(1)
4079	PENDENNIS CASTLE	4-6-0	4C	Sdn		1924	(b)	(2)
	JOHN	0-4-0ST	OC	P	1976	1939	(c)	(3)
	-	0-4-0ST	OC	P	2110	1950	(d)	(4)
D2381		0-6-0DM		Sdn		1961	(e)	(5)
A144	PWM 2176	2w2PMR		Wkm	4153		(f)	(6)
4472	FLYING SCOTSMAN	4-6-2	3C	Don	1564	1923	(g)	(7)
No. 4		0-6-0ST	OC	WB	2680	1944	(h)	(8)
	FRED	0-4-0ST	OC	AE	1908	1925	(i)	(9)
BEA 2		0-4-0ST	OC	AE	1972	1927	(j)	(4)
35029	ELLERMAN LINES	4-6-2	3C	Elh		1949	(k)	(10)
	PRIMROSE No. 2	0-6-0ST	IC	HE	3715	1952	(l)	(11)
	-	0-6-0DM		HE	2697	1944	(m)	(12)
No. 1	GLENFIELD	0-4-0CT	OC	AB	880	1902	(n)	(13)
	-	0-4-0ST	OC	AB	1931	1927	(o)	(4)
	EYU 3386	4wPM		Austin			(p)	(14)

(a) ex Great Western Preservations Ltd, Didcot, 6/1972
(b) ex Great Western Preservations Ltd, Didcot, 23/6/1972
(c) ex NCB North Nottinghamshire Area, Thoresby Colliery, 12/1972
(d) ex NCB North Nottinghamshire Area, Harworth Colliery, 4/1973
(e) ex BR Derby, 13/4/1973
(f) ex ?, c 4/1973
(g) ex BRE, Derby 30/7/1973
(h) ex Birchenwood Gas & Coke Co Ltd, Kidsgrove, Staffordshire, c 10/1973
(i) ex Yorkshire Dales Railway, Embsay, 24/10/1973
(j) ex Keighley & Worth Valley Railway, 12/1973
(k) ex Woodham Bros, Barry, 7/1/1974; to Buckminster Enterprises for sectioning 13/2/1974; ex Buckminster 4/1/1974
(l) ex Yorkshire Dales Railway 1/2/1974
(m) ex Sir Robert McAlpine & Sons Ltd, Kettering, 5/1974
(n) ex Great Western Preservations Ltd, Didcot, 1/7/1974
(o) ex Buckminster Enterprises 1/1/1975
(p) ex W. H. McAlpine, Fawley, Buckinghamshire 11/1975

(1) to Baguley-Drewry Ltd, Burton on Trent 10/1973
(2) to BR Neville Hill, Leeds, 5/10/1974; then to Steamtown, Carnforth
(3) to Steamtown, Carnforth, 15/1/1976
(4) to Market Overton Industrial Railway Association, 19/3/1976. (same site)
(5) to Steamtown, Carnforth, 19/3/1976
(6) to Steamtown, Carnforth, 23/2/1976
(7) to Steamtown, Carnforth, 5/1974
(8) to North Norfolk Railway 13/1/1976
(9) to Peterborough Railway Society, 15/2/1976

(10) to National Railway Museum, York, c 8/9/1975
(11) to Yorkshire Dales Railway 11/7/1975
(12) to Steamtown, Carnforth, 27/1/1976
(13) to Steamtown, Carnforth, 14/1/1976
(14) to Steamtown, Carnforth, 22/1/1976

Gauge; 2ft.0in.

-	0-4-0T	OC	P	2024	1942	(a)	(1)

(a) ex Rhodesia Chrome Mines Ltd c 7/1973

(1) to Welsh Highland Railway (1964) Ltd, 6/3/1976

Market Overton Industrial Railway Association

Gauge; 4ft. 8½in.

	-	0-4-0ST	OC	AB	1931	1927	(a)	(1)
	DORA	0-4-0ST	OC	AE	1973	1927	(a)	(2)
	-	0-4-0ST	OC	P	2110	1950	(a)	(1)
No. 31		0-6-0ST	IC	HC	1026	1913	(b)	(3)
	-	4wDM		FH	3887	1958	(c)	(2)
	SINGAPORE	0-4-0ST	OC	HL	3865	1936	(d)	(1)
	UPPINGHAM	0-4-0ST	OC	P	1257	1912	(e)	(2)
	ELIZABETH	0-4-0ST	OC	P	1759	1928	(f)	(2)
	-	4wDM		RH	305302	1951	(g)	(4)
	COAL PRODUCTS No.6	0-6-0ST	IC	HE	2868	1943	(h)	(5)
	SIR THOMAS ROYDEN	0-4-0ST	OC	AB	2088	1940	(i)	(6)

(a) ex Flying Scotsman Enterprises, 19/3/1976 (same site)
(b) ex W. H. McAlpine, Fawley, c 1/3/1977
(c) ex Hambleton Bros, Caistor, Lincolnshire, 7/4/1977 (prev. Fisons Ltd, Immingham)
(d) ex South Eastern Steam Centre, Ashford, Kent 25/10/1977
(e) ex Midland Railway Trust Ltd, Normanton Barracks, Sinfin, Derby 3/6/1978
(f) ex Redland Roadstone Ltd, Mountsorrel, Leicestershire 7/6/1978
(g) ex Ransome Hoffman Pollard Ltd, Newark, 17/3/1979
(h) ex NCB Glasshoughton Coke Ovens 30/3/1979
(i) ex Mark Bamford, Ellastone, 9/4/1979

(1) to Cottesmore Sidings, 21/12/1979
(2) to Cottesmore Sidings, 22/12/1979
(3) to McAlpine, Fawley, 29/5/1979
(4) to Cottesmore Sidings, 29/12/1979
(5) to Cottesmore Sidings, 15/12/1979
(6) to Asfordby Road, Melton Mowbray, for display, 10/8/1979; to Cottesmore Sidings 5/1980

EXPLANATION OF TABLES

Locomotives

The columns show in order:- title: type:cylinder position: maker: maker's number: year built: cylinder dimensions: driving wheel diameter: origin: disposal. In referring to these columns the following points should be noted.

Title. Unofficial names used by the staff but not carried by the engine are denoted by inverted commas.

Type. The Whyte system of wheel classification is used, but if wheels are not connected by outside rods they are shown as 4w, 6w as the case may be. The following abbreviations are used:

T	Side Tank	DM	Diesel Mechanical	BE	Battery Electric
PT	Pannier Tank	DE	Diesel Electric	WE	Wire Electric
ST	Saddle Tank	DH	Diesel Hydraulic		
WT	Well Tank	PM	Petrol Mechanical		
VB	Vertical Boiler	PE	Petrol Electric		
G	Geared	PMR	Petrol Mechanical Railcar		

Cylinder Position	IC	Inside Cylinders
	OC	Outside Cylinders
	VC	Vertical Cylinders

Makers. The following abbreviations are used, with lesser known builders' names being given in full.

AB	Andrew Barclay Sons & Co Ltd, Kilmarnock.
AE	Avonside Engine Co Ltd, Bristol
AP	Aveling & Porter Ltd, Rochester
B	Barclays & Co, Kilmarnock
BEV	British Electric Vehicles Ltd, Southport
Bg	E. E. Baguley Ltd, Burton on Trent
BH	Black Hawthorn & Co Ltd, Gateshead
Bton	Brighton Locomotive Works, LB&SCR
CF	Chapman & Furneaux Ltd, Gateshead
DC	Drewry Car Co Ltd, London (Suppliers only)
DK	Dick, Kerr & Co Ltd, Preston
EE	English Electric Co Ltd, Preston
EV	Ebbw Vale Steel Coal & Iron Co Ltd, Ebbw Vale
FE	Falcon Engine & Car Works Ltd, Loughborugh
FH	F. C. Hibberd & Co Ltd, London
FW	Fox Walker & Co, Bristol
GB	Greenwood & Batley Ltd, Leeds

GEC/USA	General Electric Co, USA
H	James & Frederick Howard Ltd, Bedford
HC	Hudswell Clarke & Co Ltd, Leeds
HCR	Hudswell Clarke & Rodgers, Leeds
HE	Hunslet Engine Co Ltd, Leeds
HL	Hawthorn Leslie & Co Ltd, Newcastle upon Tyne
Hu	Robert Hudson Ltd, Leeds
JF	John Fowler & Co (Leeds) Ltd
K	Kitson & Co Ltd, Leeds
KE	Kilmarnock Engineering Co Ltd
KS	Kerr, Stuart & Co Ltd, Stoke on Trent
Mkm	Markham & Co Ltd, Chesterfield
MR	Motor Rail Ltd, Bedford
MW	Manning Wardle & Co Ltd, Leeds
N	Neilson & Co, Glasgow
OK	Orenstein & Koppel AG, Berlin
P	Peckett & Sons Ltd, Bristol
RH	Ruston & Hornsby Ltd, Lincoln
RR	Rolls Royce Ltd, Shrewsbury
RS	Robert Stephenson & Co Ltd, Newcastle upon Tyne and Darlington
RSH	Robert Stephenson & Hawthorns Ltd, Newcastle upon Tyne
S	Sentinel (Shrewsbury) Ltd
Sdn	Swindon Locomotive Works, GWR
SS	Sharp Stewart & Co Ltd, Glasgow
VF	Vulcan Foundry Ltd, Newton-le-Willows
WB	W. G. Bagnall Ltd, Stafford
YE	Yorkshire Engine Co Ltd, Sheffield

Maker's Number. Reb = Rebuilt.

Year Built. The year quoted is that given on the maker's plate, or from the maker's records if the date does not appear on the plate.

Cylinder and Driving Wheel Dimensions. These apply to locomotive as new.

Origin. 'New' indicates that the locomotive was delivered by the makers to this location at the stated date (to the month where known). Transfers from elsewhere are indicated by a bracketed letter and appropriate footnote.

Disposal. Locomotives transferred to another owner or site are shown by a bracketed number with corresponding footnote. Scr = Scrapped. s/s = scrapped or sold, disposal unknown.

Explanation of tables

Quarry Machines

The information is set out in much the same way as for locomotives, but as collected information on quarry machines has not appeared before we give rather more in the way of explanation. The columns show in order:- title (if any): class description: power source and type of machine: maker: maker's number: year built: bucket capacity: jib or boom length: origin: disposal.

Title. Often machines carried no title, but major operators such as Stewarts & Lloyds Minerals Ltd gave them numbers, quoted where known; and a very few were named.

Class Description. Steam machines were most commonly referred to as '10-ton', '20-ton', etc, the 'ton' referring not to the weight but to the cutting pressure on the bucket teeth. Ruston Proctor & Co Ltd adopted these as class numbers, a No. 20 machine being a '20-ton' and so on, and these class numbers have been used in the tables, as in the manufacturer's literature. Whitaker's used a letter code but unfortunately only in a few cases do we know these, so we have had to fall back on '12 ton' etc. Ruston & Hornsby Ltd used designatory numbers for larger machines, e.g. No. 250.

Diesel and electric machines were given class numbers by Ruston Bucyrus Ltd from a scheme used by the Bucyrus Co. The early machines were described as 37B, 43B etc but this was later changed to 37RB and 43RB etc, and we have used the latter throughout for simplicity. The numbers correspond roughly with the weight of the machine in tons. Ransomes & Rapier Ltd applied class numbers such as 422, 480 etc, and also used these numbers for steam machines of the same power. The large Walking Draglines of both manufacturers incorporated 'W' in the class description — 3W, 5W for RB in ascending order of size, and W 150, W 1400 etc for R&R, the numbers again corresponding roughly to the weights.

Power Source and Type of Machine. The power source is indicated by a letter:- S — Steam: D — Diesel: DE — Diesel Electric: E — Electric: PP — Petrol-paraffin.

The two main types of machine are shovels and draglines. In simple terms, the latter were used primarily for removing overburden by dragging the bucket up the working face by a chain in a scraping motion, then slewing the bucket round to dump the load on the worked-out area; a shovel would then dig out the ore beneath. Obviously there are many variants on these according to circumstances, and digger drivers were very adept in using their machines in difficult positions. Some removal of overburden was done by 'stripping shovels' of large size. The form and duties of various specialized machines will be obvious from their names — crane, clamshell, back-acter, etc. Some machines were rail-mounted, some on crawlers or 'Caterpillar' tracks. When the type of machine is uncertain, the term 'navvy' is used.

Makers. The following abbreviations are used, with lesser known builder's names being given in full.

At	Atlantic Equipment Co, USA
BE	Bucyrus-Erie Co, USA
Berry	Henry Berry & Co Ltd, Leeds
Bu	Bucyrus Co, USA
Lima	Baldwin Lima Hamilton Co, USA
Marion	Marion Steam Shovel Co, USA
NBM	Newton, Bean & Mitchell, Bradford
Priestman	Priestman Brothers Ltd, Hull
RB	Ruston Bucyrus Ltd, Lincoln
RH	Ruston & Hornsby Ltd, Lincoln
RP	Ruston Proctor & Co Ltd, Lincoln
R&R	Ransomes & Rapier Ltd, Ipswich
S&P	Stothert & Pitt Ltd, Bath
Taylor Hubbard	Taylor Hubbard & Co Ltd, Leicester
Wh	Whitaker Bros Ltd, Leeds
Wilson	John H. Wilson & Co Ltd, Liverpool

Makers' Number and **Year Built.** These are taken from manufacturers' records in the case of the Ruston companies and from R & R; from operators' records otherwise.

Bucket Capacity and **Jib or Boom Length.** The figures come from operators' records mostly, sometimes from manufacturers. There is no hard and fast rule about the terms 'jib' and 'boom' but generally steam machines are spoken of as having jibs, and diesel and electric machines booms, particularly the larger machines.

Origin. 'New' means that the machine was supplied by the makers to this location. The months quoted are those shown as delivery dates in the makers' records; but very often machines were supplied in sections to be assembled on site (this being particularly so with large machines) so that some time elapsed before they entered service.

Transfers from other locations are shown by bracketed letters and appropriate footnotes. To save space, these footnotes also include details of any changes in bucket capacity or jib length.

Disposal. A machine transferred to another location is shown by a bracketed number and corresponding footnote. Scr = scrapped: s/s = scrapped or sold, disposal unknown. These footnotes also include known details of the individual quarries or working faces that the machine served in the system concerned, with dates where known.

Sources of Information. The principal sources of information consulted and quoted from, using the abbreviations given, are as follows. All were published by Her/His Majesty's Stationery Office.

Mineral Statistics of Great Britain. Robert Hunt.	1853-81	(MS)
Mineral Statistics of Great Britain. Geological Survey Memoirs	1882-94	(MS)
List of Quarries in the United Kingdom and the Isle of Man	1895-1934	(LQ)
Special Reports on the Mineral Resources of Great Britain:		
Part XII—Iron Ore. Geologial Survey Memoirs	1920	(GSM)
The Mesozoic Ironstone of England: The Northampton		
Sand Ironstone	1951	(NSI)
The Mesozoic Ironstone of England: The Liassic Ironstones	1952	(LI)

INDEX

Index